## Early Praise for *Mindfulness Medication*

"Stress, with its challenging and often debilitating effects, is an increasingly disruptive presence in many people's lives. This books offers practical mindfulness tools for pausing and drawing on the inner resources we can bring to managing our stress in powerful and life-affirming ways."

ZINDEL V. SEGAL, PhD, Distinguished Professor of Mood Disorders, University of Toronto, Scarborough, and co-author of *Mindfulness-Based Cognitive Therapy for Depression: A New Approach to Preventing Relapse*, Toronto, ON

"Dr. Blustein draws on his years of experience as a physician and meditation-practitioner to bring us a clear, practical and effective manual for living healthier and happier lives. As a fellow physician, I would be happy to pass his prescription on to anyone wanting to prevent illness, as well as to those in search of healing. In these times of increased stress, this means all of us!"

ADRIANNE ROSS, MD, PhD, physician, Insight Meditation teacher and instructor in Mindfulness-Based Stress Reduction, Vancouver, BC

"*Mindfulness Medication* is one of the most readable books on Mindfulness I've read. It gets right to the practical heart of Mindfulness, including tools that move the theory into real life. It builds very solidly, and is very hands on, giving you what you need to know without being bogged down. I tend to read a book through before trying exercises, and I found it hard not to stop and just start putting the exercises into practice."

NATALIE BOON, Editor, *Boon Information Services*, Toronto, ON

Early Praise for *Mindfulness Medication*

"Dr. Blustein's work on meditation is quite literally "a breath" of fresh air! This book synthesizes in a very accessible and modern way, years of study and personal practice of ancient meditation technique. His experience as a gastroenterologist has impassioned him to share a very practical model of meditation for better health and well-being."

DONNA FRIESEN, Former Oil & Gas Executive,
Calgary, AB

"Dr. Blustein has done a great job of making basic ideas around mindfulness accessible and easy to implement for beginners and beyond. His style is friendly, personal, and easy to read, as he draws from both his personal mindfulness experience and decades of work with patients suffering from unexplained physical symptoms. This is a great place to start your journey into mindfulness and self-discovery!"

LINDA E. CARLSON, PhD, RPsych,
Enbridge Research Chair in Psychosocial Oncology
Alberta Innovates-Health Solutions Health Scholar
Professor, Department of Oncology, Cumming School of Medicine
Adjunct Professor, Department of Psychology, University of Calgary
& Clinical Psychologist, Director of Research,
Department of Psychosocial Resources, Tom Baker Cancer Centre
Calgary, AB

# Mindfulness
# Medication

Dear Russell,
I hope this book
will be of value
for you.
Warm Regards,
Phil. B.

Published by Mindfulness Medication Publishing

E-mail: mindfulnessmedication@gmail.com

Website: www.thebreathproject.org

First Paperback Edition – Second Impression

19 18 17 16 15 — 2 3 4 5 6 7 8 9

**Library and Archives Canada Cataloguing in Publication**

Blustein, Phil, 1950 –, author

Mindfulness medication : A physician's prescription for stress relief / Phil Blustein, MD.

Includes bibliographical references.

Issued in print and electronic formats.

ISBN: 978 – 0 – 9918520 – 0 – 0 (pbk). — ISBN: 978 – 0 – 9918520 – 1 – 7 (pdf).— ISBN: 978 – 0 – 9918520 – 2 – 4 (html)

1. Stress management. 2. Stress (Psychology). I. Title.

RA785.B68 2015                  155.9'042                  C2015-907492-9

C2015-907493-7

TECHNICAL CREDITS:

Editing: Crescent McKeag, *Calgary Writing Services*, Calgary, Alberta

Front Cover Photograph and Author Portrait: Peter Beech, Photographer, Calgary, Alberta, <www.airshots.ca>

Illustrations: Scott Lewis, Vancouver, British Columbia, <www.storyboardlabel.com>

Design & Production: Jeremy Drought, *Last Impression Publishing Service*, Calgary, Alberta

Printed in Canada by *Houghton Boston*, Saskatoon, Saskatchewan, Canada

# Mindfulness Medication

## A Physician's Prescription For Stress Relief

Phil Blustein, MD

Mindfulness Medication Publishing

CALGARY, ALBERTA

*for Shira and Jared*
*who fill my heart with love and joy*
*and have taught me that wisdom is present at any age*

# Contents

# Acknowledgements

**I HAVE HAD MANY TEACHERS** that have influenced my path. I would like to extend my appreciation for these wonderful teachers, who have influenced humanity with great knowledge, insight and compassion.

They include the Buddha and many teachers of Spirit Rock and the Insight Meditation Society; Marshall Rosenberg with his wonderful work on nonviolent communication; Margaret Paul, Erika Chopich, Hal and Sidra Stone, and John Pollard for their insight on the inner child.

I have been blessed by the following people, each of whom has offered helpful support: Crescent McKeag for her great editing; Scott Lewis for his playful and creative illustrations; Shelley Cooper for her wonderful computer skills; and Jeremy Drought of *Last Impression Publishing Service* for his expert book design.

I would like to further dedicate this book to my family, friends, patients and readers, and finally to my own mind, which creates so many opportunities for me to learn on a continual basis.

# *Introduction*

**D**O YOU EVER HAVE THE FEELING that you were born into this world and someone forgot to give you the driver's manual for your own mind? One day you're sitting in a fancy new luxury model, the next, you're driving around in a clunker. Some days your mind seems to run on and on but you can't seem to find the brake. You may find yourself heading from one disaster to another and the steering wheel won't respond. You may want to direct your mind in a way that's more peaceful and forgiving but it's as if you're sitting in a car that you have no control over. Suddenly, you're just a passenger in your own mind, not the driver.

So how do you find the driver's manual for your mind so that you're not just a passenger on a wild ride? There is no one right answer, however, there is hope. With some reading and diligent practice, think of it as driver training, you will begin to really get a handle on how your mind works.

I have been a doctor now for over thirty years. I work in a hospital where I specialize in things that go wrong with the digestive system. During my time as a medical specialist, I began to notice more and more, how much of a tremendous role stress seemed to play in my patients' medical problems. Patients would come to the hospital with symptoms of chest pain, heartburn, abdominal pain, diarrhea or constipation. When I asked what had been going on just before the onset of their symptoms, they often told me that they had been feeling very stressed about family, work or financial issues. They hadn't even considered that there might be a relationship between their physical symptoms and all the stress in their lives. If you can effectively deal with your own stress, there is the real possibility that you will have fewer medical issues in your life!

I myself, like everyone else, have struggled with stress and a mind that wasn't always so kind to me. I could be happy one moment, sad the next. I felt, at times, that I had no control over what would pop into my head. I would react automatically to whatever was occurring in my life. I just wanted more calmness and joy, but I was at the mercy of my mind. It became my primary mission to find the best way to deal with this.

I became a doctor, read a lot, went to therapy and studied Eastern and Western approaches to stress reduction and the workings of the human mind. It's taken me a long time, but I can honestly say that slowly, I have started to be present in life from a place of greater joy. I'm not so much the victim of my thoughts anymore. I have a greater sense of clarity and understanding about what is happening in my thoughts from moment to moment and this process is constantly evolving.

You and I both have to deal with some stress every single day. It's a part of life! However, it's for exactly this reason, the fact that you face stress everyday and somehow keep soldiering on, that you may not realize when your stress is building up and causing you actual physical harm. Of course there's no magic pill or day surgery that will cure a high-pressure job, too little time, too many demands, a bad relationship, or the daily juggling act of kids and career. You can always wait until something serious goes wrong and then a specialist like me might be able to patch you up and send you back out there, but I have a wonderful alternative.

I present to you an integrated, novel approach encompassing the best techniques for reducing the stress in your life that I could find, from my experience with both Eastern and Western practices. In essence, this approach employs mindfulness to hold your physical and mental stress and inner-child dialogue to change the paradigm of your thinking which is leading to a painful existence. I recommend this approach to you now as a *pre*-scription, a life-insurance policy that will go a long way toward keeping you healthy and well and out of my office. While it's unrealistic to think that you'll ever be free of stress completely, a sense of freedom and happiness comes from the ability to be fully present during these stressful experiences, without amplifying their trauma or identifying with them. When it comes to stressful events, it doesn't matter what they are, it matters how you are with them.

This book is meant to be used; to be revisited again and again. It really is all about you! What you put into it, in terms of attempting what I suggest by processing and practicing, will be what you get out of it. Do what works for you and take from it what you can. Every little bit of practice will help. Return to reading the rest of the book, in sequence, whenever you're able to, as each section builds on the one before. In understanding lies real stress relief.

This book serves as a practical sequential guide that will bring you to an understanding of how your mind works the way it does and why it does so. There are effective techniques outlined here that will help you to deal with your stress right at the very moment it occurs. There are also approaches that will help you to change the underlying mechanisms at the root of your unhappiness. Some parts of this book will appeal to you, while others may not seem to apply.

I'm looking forward to sharing with you what I have found to be personally helpful for both my patients and myself. Hopefully, this will provide you with your own insight into how to live in this world with greater peace and satisfaction. I offer this book to you as a reflection of my belief in service. I believe that all of us are connected through our shared humanity and our universal mental suffering. Stress affects every human being on the road of life, but you're in the driver's seat now. Here's the manual you were looking for.

*Dr. Phil Blustein*
*Calgary, Alberta*
*December, 2014*

# 1

# *What Your Body Has in Mind*
# *When You Don't Mind Your Body*

STRESS IS NOT THE ONLY CAUSE of illness but it can certainly make what you do have worse. People get sick for multiple reasons, which include genetics, lifestyle issues and environmental toxins. Stress is something that all people experience and it can lead to physical problems as well. Stress reflects how you perceive and interpret the events in your life. Western medicine is fantastic at identifying and treating physical ailments, but it doesn't emphasize and prioritize the contribution of underlying stress to these medical issues. Most people deal with the consequence, and not the cause, of an illness.

I'd like to introduce you to some of my actual patients so you can start to connect the dots for yourself:

Larry is a big man. He has a big appetite, a big family and when he has diarrhea it's a big problem. He has a long-standing history of Crohn's disease (an inflammatory condition of the bowel) and had already undergone surgery. He was doing quite well, until several months ago. When I inquired, he told me about having to care for his father who had recently died, and that he was laid off from a job that he had been working at for the last ten years. The economy forced him to take a new job that he really hated, for less pay. He and his wife were constantly battling over finances. His diarrhea and abdominal pain had become progressively worse and worse until he ended up with a bowel obstruction that could only be corrected by yet another surgery. He had ignored a growing problem for a long time but his body hadn't. I was frustrated that I could only try to fix the damage done after the fact, instead of helping Larry learn how to interfere with the progression of his disease while he still had a chance to avoid the knife.

Mika is another of my patients but she is representative of so many. She had recently come from Thailand to work in Canada. It was a new job, a new language and a new culture. She had left her family back home and they were depending on her to send back money to support them. Clearly under tremendous pressure, she began to experience problems with abdominal pain and an irregular bowel pattern with alternating diarrhea and constipation, gas and bloating. She also began having difficulty sleeping and was experiencing headaches and fatigue, which are often some of the first symptoms of ongoing stress. All of her medical tests came back normal and I diagnosed her with Irritable Bowel Syndrome. Again, Mika's body was reacting to the levels of stress in her life and I was forced to just help her treat her symptoms, knowing that until she lowered her stress levels, she was in for more suffering, pain and grief.

What's common to both of these patients and many others, is that their symptoms are really secondary to, or aggravated by, the stress in their lives. Their symptoms are what western medicine calls 'stress induced'. If they had been able to understand what their stress levels were doing to their bodies before it made them sick and if they also had some help to then reduce their stress, perhaps I may never have met them at all!

Let's start by taking a look at what both Eastern and Western philosophies have to say about how you create and deal with stress. Both schools of thought offer tremendous insights. Rather than seeing them as separate, I have tried to integrate the tools and concepts that I have found to be most useful, regardless of point of origin. This integrative approach merges the best of Eastern and Western philosophy, medicine, and psychology as a means to understand the mind, how each of us creates stress, and how you can best learn to manage and minimize it.

# Autonomic Physical and Psychological Responses

Have you ever had to consciously tell your heart to beat, or your lungs to breathe, in order to make sure that they were doing their jobs? Your heartbeat and breathing are both examples of what scientists call autonomic involuntary behaviours. That's a fancy way of saying that these biological activities carry on independently, without you having to be actively aware of what's going on. The same can be said for a lot of the mental activities that carry on in your life. As an example, see if any of the following scenarios are familiar to you:

- Have you ever had an experience where you drove from one spot to another and have suddenly realized that you don't recall driving the last few blocks, or even the whole trip sometimes?
- Have you ever mindlessly eaten something without really tasting any of it because you were thinking about something else?
- Have you ever reacted to a situation with such intensity and anger that your response was way over the top and then you wondered later, "Where did all that come from?"
- Do you have an inner voice that's constantly critical and which seems to always have something negative to say, as it evaluates your actions and appearance and how you compare to others?

Your mind is constantly thinking, evaluating and judging, as well as going over what happened in the past and your plans for the future. This is, in fact, the normal function of the mind. Just as your heart beats and your lungs breathe, your mind thinks. It's what it does naturally, but unlike the moment-to-moment activities of the heart, or the lungs, the automatic thoughts that go through your head are something that can be observed, examined, changed and released. Your thoughts are the product of your experiences, your history, your biology and most importantly, your habits. External events conspire with the internal workings of your mind to create stress.

But you're not simply a robot that follows the automatic directions of your mind. You can actually think about your thoughts. You can examine what's going on in your mind and what your mind says to you. Because your mind has the ability to literally think about itself, you can often find ways in which your habitual patterns of thought are maintaining a stress response.

The physical stress response that occurs when your mind perceives a threat is a powerful one. When Larry first lost his job, he thought constantly about how catastrophic this turn of events was. He felt that it was a threat to his financial and social status and potentially a threat to not only his own survival, but also the survival of his family. His body in turn helped him out by releasing adrenaline and cortisol, the body's alarm bells, as well as other chemicals. These chemicals prepared him to fight or run, as if the origin of the threat were a predatory animal out for his blood. Physically, his heartbeat and breathing rate increased. His blood pressure rose and his mouth went dry. The pupils of his eyes grew bigger and his muscles received more blood in preparation for an immediate action like running or punching, but there was no one to run from and certainly no one to punch!

As he continued worrying about his situation, his body could not sustain the initial stress response. It tried to adapt but couldn't keep it up. He wasn't sleeping well. His immune system also stopped working very well, so he got every cold and flu bug going around. He was tired all the time, because it's hard work for the body to stay ready to fight, or run, around the clock. His digestive system was a mess. Needless to say, that even when Larry got a new job, he was still worried about making ends meet and his body continued to 'help him' by keeping up all the stress responses as best it could, until one by one, his body's systems and processes began to break down.

Larry, of course wasn't aware of what his body was up to in response to his constant worrying. He only knew that he didn't feel the best and it was getting worse not better. The body really tries not to bother you with trivial things like the fact that your heart is beating, your food is being digested and your lungs are supplying oxygen one breath at a time, until and unless it really can't cope anymore. That's when you'd come to me, but by then it's often too little too late. By learning to recognize the early symptoms of too much stress and what both your body and your mind are trying to tell you, you can intervene earlier in the process.

I think that you can probably relate to the fact that your life is hectic and often you feel a sense of stress about the events that you encounter. You know that there's a problem and it would be great if you could have some tools to help you deal with your issues. The next chapters outline how your mind works to create an intimate connection between your thoughts and your emotional and physical responses, but let's cut right to some solutions.

Eastern philosophies offer some powerful antidotes to the stress response that are being incorporated more and more into the frontiers of Western medical practices. The Eastern concept of *mindfulness* allows you to create some much needed space in the mind as it were; so that you can then use the Western based techniques of *inquiry* and *inner-child dialogue* to understand the origins of your belief system.

Your stress response really depends on how you react to your own thoughts. *Mindfulness* is simply the process of trying to be aware, in an accepting and non judgmental way, of what you're thinking about, what you're feeling, and what your body is up to. *Inquiry* and *inner-child sialogue* are based on investigations into how belief systems and patterns of behaviour develop and persist from childhood to affect your adult responses.

The technique of *mindfulness* allows you to be present and aware of what's on your mind, without identifying quite as strongly with the stories that you habitually tell yourself and without needing to change anything about the experience you're actually having. It's a way of practicing how to not get so carried away. It's this bringing together of Western insight into the nature and origin of thought, and the Eastern tradition and practice of *mindfulness* that can provide the tools to live, not free of thought, but with the freedom to have your thoughts along with an extra-helping of peace of mind. When you get better at minding your mind, your body won't have a mind of its own!

## Practice

1. Think of times in the past when you felt sick that you now know were related to stress.
2. How do you personally experience stress in your thoughts, feelings and body?

## Summary

- *Stress* can make you sick or make what physical problems you do have much worse.
- Your thoughts are what trigger the body's stress response.
- Once the body's stress response is triggered, it continues to affect you without you necessarily being aware of it until it can no longer cope and its resources are exhausted.
- The technique of combining Eastern mindfulness practices with Western investigation into belief systems and the nature and origin of your thoughts can provide excellent stress relief.

## 2

# Meet Your Mind

**I**N THE LAST CHAPTER, YOU WERE introduced to the fact that once your mind starts thinking that there's a threat, something going wrong in your internal or external environment, it starts a physical process in your body whose initial purpose is to help you to better deal with that threat. If you don't think that the threat is gone, then your body begins to not work as well, bit-by-bit, until eventually you'll need a doctor. However, the initial perception of a threat occurs in your mind as a thought. What one person thinks is very threatening and stressful someone else may not.

Mika, my patient from Thailand, for example, grew up with very deadly snakes in her home country and has been afraid of them since childhood. Larry has a pet snake and it sits wrapped around his shoulders and watches TV with him. What Mika thinks of as stressful, in this case the sight of a snake, Larry thinks of as fun or interesting. Their thoughts about the same snake are very different.

So if stress is dependent on your thoughts about something, let's take a look at thoughts, what they are and where they come from. Some insights into how your mind works can help you better manage the stress in your life.

I'm going to lead you through some exercises that will open the door to understanding your own thought processes. This is a step-by-step journey of personal discovery that will give you an understanding of your own mind, the driver of your actions.

## How many thoughts do you have?

The average person has about 60,000 thoughts a day. Further, 90% of these thoughts are the same repetitive notions playing over and over. You're constantly thinking, but most people are not consciously aware of the type of thought passing through, how often it comes around, or what triggers that particular thought. Your mind is like a popcorn machine, constantly popping up thoughts, but you're only consciously aware of a small percentage of them.

Let's try something. See if you can count every thought that comes into your consciousness. Even if the thoughts seem to be something along the lines of the following:

- "This is stupid."
- "I wonder how long it's been."
- "I need to do laundry and get to the store."
- "Is that one thought or two?"

Just try to count them as best you can.

 Set a timer for two minutes. There are countdown timers available online, as various apps, or you can set an egg timer, watch, or cell-phone timer. Close your eyes. Count your thoughts and return to reading the book after you're through.

How many thoughts did you have? Were you surprised by how many you had? They certainly aren't permanent. If you wait long enough a new thought will always come up. Imagine how many thoughts you're not even aware of.

As you begin to observe your mind, you'll notice that it's always active and that it tends to say the same things over and over again. Let's admit it, most of the time we all have pretty boring minds.

You probably get so caught up in your thoughts, just by force of habit, that even when you're sitting silently you're not really at rest. If you mention to someone that you're going to go away on a silent retreat, often his or her initial reaction is, "I couldn't do that. I could never sit still. My mind is always thinking." Of course it is! Thinking is what the mind does. It's the natural function of the mind, but you're not necessarily at its mercy.

## What's the nature of your thoughts?

Once you start looking in on your thoughts you'll probably notice that most of them seem to be about reliving the past, or planning for/imagining the future. Few of them tend to be about the present moment.

Let's jump right into another exercise. When a thought pops up, I want you to name the time period when it seems to be occurring. You can say past, present, or future.

 Set your timer for two minutes again. Close your eyes and note when, in time, your thoughts are occurring. Return to the book when you're done.

Were your thoughts predominantly about events that happened in the past? Were your thoughts predominantly about events that may occur in the future? Or were they focused on the present moment as it unfolded?

The future hasn't happened and therefore doesn't exist as yet and the past has already gone by and therefore also doesn't exist in the here and now. The present, this very moment, is the only time that you have any real control over. If your thoughts tend, as most do, to the future or the past, you're missing out on a lot of the right now. You're generally not fully present to the beauty of the only moment in time that truly exists!

Another aspect of thought is that it's largely concerned with judging, comparing and criticizing. Your mind is constantly evaluating every external and internal situation that you encounter.

Here's another exercise to help you understand your own thoughts. This time you're going to pick a word that basically describes what the thought is about as it happens. Say something to yourself like criticizing, or planning, or worrying, or judging, or remembering. You don't have to say your description words out loud but you can if you like.

 Set your trusty timer for two minutes. Close your eyes. Note what your thoughts are about and return to the text when you're done.

So what were your thoughts about? Were they about an argument you had with your partner yesterday? Judging your boss for what he said to you? Criticizing yourself for something you did, or said, to your family? Minds are often not very friendly!

It's important to become familiar with what your mind is saying to you. Try these short, two-minute exercises whenever you have a moment during the day. The more familiar you are with your own mind, the easier it will be for you to intervene in your stress responses.

## How easy is it to be distracted by your thoughts?

Now that you're getting a bit more familiar with your own mind, let's try a few more experiments.

I would like you to close your eyes and simply observe your breath. This time, you're going to count to ten. Breathe in and out. That counts as one cycle. Mentally count one. Another cycle of inhalation and exhalation is number two and mentally count two. Continue like this to a count of ten. If a different thought arises, other than mentally watching your breath-cycles and counting them, then start right back at the beginning at one. Simple right?

It's important that you really try to do all of the experiments and practice suggestions in this book. Real positive change comes from doing, not just from reading.

 Give this breath exercise a try right now and then return to the book when you're through. Set your timer for two minutes and close your eyes.

So how far did you get? Sometimes I can't get beyond one or two breath-cycles before another thought pops up! Your mind is constantly thinking and as amazing as it is, you probably can't even maintain your concentration for ten breaths. It can be very difficult for you to develop the concentration to be mentally present and fully aware of what's going on in the here and now. Your mind is like a little hummingbird, flitting from one sensation, thought or perception to the next. Your thoughts are very powerful and can easily pull you away from what you're doing. You can get carried away into your various mental worlds at the drop of a hat, which leads us to the next concept.

## Can your thoughts be just on the present moment?

As it turns out, both Eastern and Western observations confirm that we all have the ability to focus attention on what's happening in the present moment, right in the here and now, and that when we do so, it silences and calms the mind. Even if you only manage this present-focus for a short period of time, what time you do spend in the present, is time that takes away from the habitual thoughts of the past or future. Contemplating the past and the future also just happens to be where most of your stressful thoughts arise. You probably worry most about either what's going to happen or what has already happened. What's happening right now, in this very instant, is likely considerably less stressful.

Let's try an experiment to see if you can bring those pesky, flitting little hummingbird-thoughts back into the present. Close your eyes tightly and bring all of your focus to the sensation of tension around your eyes. Squeeze your eyes even more tightly closed and feel which of your muscles are tightening in your face, between your eyes and in your forehead. Then just let it all go, release the tension and open your eyes.

Give this exercise a try right now and then return to the book when you're through.

Try it again and really focus on scrunching your eyes closed and feeling the tension in your eyes as well as around them. When you fix your concentration on doing something like this, I think you'll find that it pushes any other thoughts of yesterday or tomorrow right out of your mind. There's just what's happening right at this moment.

What is it that you like to do that you're passionate about? Is it skiing, dancing, cooking, painting, gardening, photography or playing hockey? At those times when you're deeply engrossed in a favourite activity does time stand still, or do other thoughts come into your consciousness? When you're totally present in what you are doing, the only thoughts that exist tend to be about the activity you are engaged in. You already have the ability to quiet your mind and make it focus and that just happens to be a characteristic of the human mind that you can put to use for reducing your stress. I know what you're saying is probably something like, "So scrunching my eyes reduces stress?" and the simple answer is, well yes it does, but it's just a small part of a bigger picture.

## Are thoughts permanent?

As you've no doubt noticed during the preceding exercises, thoughts come and go very frequently. Most of us normally do not have the ability to consistently maintain concentration on one thought. Even if you're generally feeling sad, angry, or happy, within a short time your mind will still drift from thought to thought. If each thought is that important and meaningful why don't thoughts stay around longer than they do? The tricky thing about any thought is that while you find yourself immersed in it, it feels permanent. It feels as though it's the complete picture, your total reality. You feel as if it will last forever. However, if you wait it out, often just a little longer, that thought will actually pass and then you'll have, at least temporarily, a break from it.

If you can think of your thoughts as clouds that form and change, vanish and reform, rather than as things that are true, absolute and permanent, it may help you to de-stress. A lot of what you're thinking when you're stressed is just a string of hypothetical 'what-ifs'. When you bring some awareness to a particularly stressful moment, you can let the natural inclination of the mind to move on, work to your advantage.

Now I'd like you to really consider how long a thought actually tends to last for you personally and whether or not it's something that's permanent and unchanging. See if you can experience your thought's cloud-like, temporary nature.

Let's try this experiment. Keep track of your thoughts. Specifically, observe how long they last, how they change or jump around and how sometimes they just pass away and another thought comes up to take their place.

 Set your timer again for two minutes. Close your eyes and note how long your thoughts last.

Were any of your thoughts permanent?

## The Nature of Thoughts

Where is a thought?
What is a thought?
Can you touch it?
Can you feel it?
Empty of form
When a thought comes
Does it hold you tightly?
Invisible chains
Real as steel
Full of form
Thought is empty
Thought has form
Is thought empty form?
Is thought formed emptiness?
What is true?
What is real?

## Where do thoughts come from?

When you start observing your thoughts, you might notice that they seem to arise spontaneously without an apparent thinker behind them. It may seem that your mind is working independently of you, or your conscious control. It might even seem like your mind has a mind of its own!

Let's meet your mind again in the following exercise. Bring your attention to your thoughts as they arise and keep in mind whether you're consciously and intentionally producing these thoughts yourself, or whether they are just arising spontaneously.

 You know the routine. Set your timer for a two-minute commitment. Close your eyes and this time notice if you're consciously and purposely producing your thoughts.

Did you know what your mind was going to say ahead of time? Where did the thoughts seem to be coming from? Who or what's generating the thoughts? If *you* were generating your thoughts *why wouldn't you know what your next thought was going to be?* Just think about it for a couple of minutes and see where it takes you.

## Does one thought lead to another?

Your thoughts are like a game of dominos, one domino hitting another domino that then creates this train of thoughts. It's as if the thoughts are being produced independently of any person behind them. What goes on in one thought, triggers a relationship to another thought that then presents itself. For example, you may be outside one day and see a bird. From your memory, the image triggers your history with and knowledge of, that type of bird. Something like the following internal conversation might take place:

*What a beautiful bird! I remember seeing that bird when I was on holiday. I really should plan a holiday for this winter. I hate the cold of winter. I need to buy a new winter jacket because the one I have isn't warm enough. I really was pretty stupid in buying that last winter jacket. It cost way too much and it really wasn't what I wanted. How could I have made such a mistake? I do that all the time.*

Just from seeing a bird you could end up anywhere!

It's a real discovery to understand that, what's on your mind is really just a flow of thoughts, each triggering the next, without any conscious activity, or sometimes even any real meaning, necessarily behind it. Thoughts seem to have a life and energy of their own. In response to an external or internal sensation, a thought arises, which triggers a memory of another event that then leads to a subsequent thought. Each thought is dependent on the preceding thought until a new sensation comes along.

Thoughts are just reflections of a complex interplay between physiological and psychological activity and are based on your previous experiences and patterns. By recognizing that your thoughts actually occur independently, in a meandering and domino-like fashion, they should have less power over you. You can observe thought production as a process occurring outside of your conscious control, like your heartbeat, or your fingernail growth. You're simply watching a game of dominos. Your thoughts are not you; they are just passing through.

Let's try this exercise to examine the flow of your thoughts. Try to notice how one thought is related to the next. See if you can recognize when one thought has triggered another. See if you can get a feeling for the whole domino effect.

 Set your timer for two minutes. Close your eyes. Notice if there's a connection between your thoughts and return to this chapter after you've finished.

Were you able to see if there was a connection between one thought and the next? We all have deeply embedded memories of our experiences and there are multiple, unconscious, mental connections that occur between these memories.

## Practice

In an attempt to train your mind to start becoming aware of the nature of your thoughts on a more regular basis, here are a few more exercises that I suggest you set some time aside to do every day.

1. Whenever a thought arises and you're consciously aware of it, simply note to yourself the word 'thinking'.
2. Take five to ten minutes in the morning before getting up, or in the evening before going to sleep, to observe your mind and its thoughts. Sometimes this exercise is harder to do if you're tired but see what works best for you. Observe how your thoughts arise spontaneously, are often connected to the preceding thought and are impermanent in nature. Focus on the idea that 'your thoughts are not you, they are just passing through'.
3. Pick something that will serve as a cue for you that occurs during your average day and use it as a reminder to simply observe your thoughts for a moment before you act on them, just as you've been doing throughout this chapter. Your cue could be as simple as sitting down to eat a meal, getting ready to go for a walk, picking up your phone to make a call, going into the bathroom, sitting in your car for a moment before driving, whatever works for you. Stick a *Post-it* note up somewhere to remind you that it's your intention to focus on your thoughts in that situation. Make it a habit and do what it takes to make it stick!

## Summary

- You have many, many thoughts in a day.
- You're probably not often aware of your thoughts.
- You're usually thinking about the past and planning for the future but are not often really present to the moment that's actually happening right now.
- Thoughts are often evaluating, criticizing or judging your experience.
- Thoughts have a temporary, impermanent nature.
- Thoughts arise spontaneously.
- Thoughts trigger other thoughts based on your previously conditioned experiences and habits.

# 3
# The Origin of Thoughts

## What are the stories you tell yourself?

IN THE LAST CHAPTER YOU INVESTIGATED the nature of individual thoughts, how they arise and flow and then move on. In this chapter, I'm going to have you take a look at how these thoughts can link together habitually in what becomes your own personal belief system. A belief system is really just a pattern of stories that you have been taught or have learned since childhood, or that you have developed in response to your own experiences. It's how you frame and understand the things that you encounter in the world around you.

You have created a personal belief system about everything you have ever come across, every new discovery, every interaction and every activity, in order to fit things in with what you already know. You never just experience something without also experiencing the story that you then create about the event, based on your personal belief system. This is part of how one thought leads to another in patterns that tend to repeat themselves. It's a normal part of your brain's functioning to try to make sense of the world by relating new things to what you're already familiar with. However, what's helpful to you in providing meaning and context for novel experiences can also be harmful to you if you have developed a belief system that encourages a stress response.

For example, when you look at another person, you project your belief system onto him or her. This helps you to decide if someone is to be approached as a friend or feared as a threat. But your first impressions, your beliefs, your patterns and ·

23

your stories are not necessarily true. People are often afraid of my patient Larry when they first meet him. He's a big man and a little scary looking, but you couldn't ask for a nicer person.

We all form immediate opinions about the people we meet based on prior experiences, our cultures, our previously formed opinions and our upbringings. We form judgments about people without even having talked to them and without knowing who they really are and those judgments could be incorrect. If your belief system encourages you to judge a person negatively, then of course your behaviour toward that person will reflect that judgment. You could be in immediate and stressful conflict with someone based on a habitual response pattern triggered by his or her clothing, smile, or hair color.

Many times, if people are acting, or dressing, in ways that don't fit with how you believe they should be behaving, or looking, then you most likely react negatively to them. However, what you're actually doing is reacting to a behaviour that you see in those people that you reject or deny in yourself. For example, if you see someone who is dressed in what you feel is a sloppy manner; you may find yourself thinking negative thoughts about him or her. You're really rejecting the idea of 'being sloppy' yourself and so, you reject the characteristic when you see it in another person as well.

Perhaps it was a notion that you first formed in your childhood. Your parents may have initially defined "sloppy" for you as a negative characteristic. When you see someone who is dressed in what you describe as a sloppy fashion, you're really just reinforcing the idea that you reject that quality in yourself. An understanding of belief systems and patterns can allow you to see that judgments are more about your own history than about the person, event, or situation being judged.

You have views about money, health, and relationships, about everything! But these judgments are really just stories that extend beyond the actual reality of the event itself, or the new person that you're meeting for the first time. These stories are simply your belief system at work trying to help you negotiate and understand your daily environment. Despite the fact that your belief system seems true for you at any given time, it's really just a set of interpretations, or tales, that you tell yourself.

You have internal and external sensations that are constantly demanding your attention, but what's instantly created in response to these circumstances is a story... your story. Even your thoughts, as they pop up out of nowhere, are immediately captured and slotted into existing patterns. Your mind doesn't record the original experience like a computer. It remembers the conditioned, reactive story that you created around the initial event, sensation, or perception and that becomes your reality. You completely forget the original event and only see the situation from the perspective of your own story.

Isn't it fascinating that we all lead our lives through the ways in which we look at the world? We never see the world objectively, or how it really is. We can only perceive it through the unique filters of our belief systems and the stories that those systems tell us.

Let's take a look now at how your mind reacts to the internal and external sensations that you're receiving. I'm going to suggest various images for you to think about and I'd like you to just notice what stories occur for you in response to the original thought.

Close your eyes and think about someone you don't like. Just sit a moment and notice the thoughts that arise. Try to recognize the story that comes up in response to the original thought. What is it you tell yourself about this person?

Next I'd like you to think about a person or a pet that you love. Again, just familiarize yourself with the stories that arise. These stories are just your belief system at work.

Choose to think about someone that is very neutral to you, such as the newspaper delivery person, or the person at the checkout at the grocery store. You don't know these people very well at all. Observe the thoughts that you have about them. Remember that you're simply exploring the makeup of your own mind.

Next, think about your work and observe the thoughts and stories that arise.

Usually when you think about someone you love, your story about that person will characterize him or her as this wonderful, happy, supportive and caring individual. When you look at someone you don't like, your thoughts and stories about that individual will reveal characteristics like negativity, selfishness and aggression. Your stories are hard at work. Even just walking down the street, your belief system has something to say about almost everything and everyone. You might see someone with tattoos and/or body piercings and think about that person in a certain way. Someone else could view the same individual in exactly the opposite fashion, because his or her belief system has something else to say. So now you have an idea that what goes on around you is filtered through the stories that you create in response to your belief system. Let's look a little closer at the stories themselves.

## Do stories change?

You may have had the experience of having been in a relationship where originally you were in love and your partner could do no wrong. Unfortunately, over time, this perspective may have changed and in the end, now that the relationship is over, you view your former partner in a totally different and negative way. The same person can therefore be viewed very differently over time.

A friend may have acted in a way that you felt was rude, or mean and then you discover that they have suffered a significant loss recently and are grieving. Your story about this friend instantly changes from an unfavorable to a favorable one and you may feel caring and concerned where you were angry and hurt only moments before. The source of your stress is not the person so much as the story, or in other words, how you've interpreted the person's behaviour.

Similarly, the beautiful new car you bought eventually just becomes a means of transportation, a money pit for repairs, or ultimately out of date and burdensome. You may even come to dislike it abruptly on seeing a nicer, more modern and flashy vehicle. Your stories can instantly change, depending on the circumstances, at any given moment. You should not hold any of them as a fixed, unchanging belief.

Hindsight is 20/20, but for right now seeing better is just perfect and I want you to start to view your stories as things that can and do change. Often, when you look back at stressful events in your life, you wonder what all the fuss was about. It just doesn't seem that bad once you've gone through it and you know it all worked out. Almost all of the stress that you're experiencing will work itself out one way or another, but the harm that you do yourself, as you go through a stressful event, is something that can be changed. You just have to see today's stressful events with that 20/20 vision of hindsight!

Think of a time when a story that you told yourself about a person, situation or event, changed. Let's explore belief systems and stories a bit further in order to understand how you can use these concepts to combat stress.

## Are your stories true?

One of the biggest and most helpful questions that you can ask yourself when you're stressed is simply, "Is this true?" Your automatic stress-filled response will most likely be a hysterical, "Well of course it is or I wouldn't be stressed!" By now you know that most of your stress comes from the story you tell yourself, not the event that you think is causing your stress. You also know that your story is probably going to change.

It's a reasonable course of action to examine and fact-check the story that you're trying to tell yourself while the stressful event is actually happening. You'll usually find that you've made a lot of assumptions, quite a few jumping to conclusions, some catastrophizing (i.e., thinking of the worst that could possibly happen) sprinkled with a bit of foretelling the future. Could you look at the story and see it another way?

Your beliefs are held as truths. However, the stories you tell yourself are your own relative personal truths and they reflect your unique perception of the world. As I mentioned before, another individual might look at a similar situation and see something completely opposite about it. Neither position may be absolutely true! Problems arise when you hold onto a belief rigidly without questioning it.

When it snows, one person might be happy as it means they can ski, while his or her neighbor is stressed because that person has to shovel the driveway. For now, simply allow yourself to be open to the reality that your stories are true for you only and there is more than one way to look at any situation.

 Consider the following topics and see what beliefs or stories come up when you think of them. Afterward, try to look at the same topics in a different way. What would someone say who disagreed with your view on these topics? Briefly examine your beliefs about politics, homosexuality, abortion and religion.

## Where do your stories come from?

Your stories are unique to you. No one else has the same stories. How you look at marriage, work, or finances, is shaped by your belief system and the stories it generates. These in turn, are all influenced by the belief systems that you were exposed to by your parents, relatives, friends and caregivers. You may also have been exposed to belief systems through various media, in your school, in your workplace, as well as in society in general. You adopted bits and pieces of these belief systems and subsequently shaped what was to become your own unique belief system. Most of what comprises your belief system originated in your childhood and came to you via your parents or caregivers.

 Can you think of a belief that you hold that came to you through your parent(s)/caregivers? What did they believe about that subject? Is your belief different at all? Think about whether your own experiences, your friends, or society may have also influenced this belief. Your beliefs are likely shaped, in part, by all of these inputs but most of the groundwork was laid when you were very young. Your stories and beliefs are further influenced by habits, contexts, and experiences. You're constantly shaping your belief system in response to what goes on both around you and in the arena of your mind.

## Why do you have these stories?

Your childhood is a key component in understanding how you created the belief system that leads to your stories. You initially created a belief system early on in your childhood, which was modeled predominantly on your parents', or caregivers' ideas. As a child, you were very vulnerable and naturally dependent on your caregivers.

Children adopt their parents' standards and beliefs in an attempt to deal with the need for safety and love, as well as an understandable fear of abandonment. If they are "good children" by acting in a way such that their parents would approve, then they feel safer and accepted. Remember, that as a child you internalized much of your own parents' or caregivers' belief systems. Subsequently, your exposure to friends, extended family, media, society and religious attitudes also worked to shape your belief system.

Genetics also contribute to a child's personality traits and how he or she responds to the world. A child's personality may be naturally inclined to be open, closed, friendly, suspicious, frightened or exploring. When an internal or external sensation is received, the mind compares it to the internalized belief system and memories of prior exposures to similar sensations. The sensation is rapidly labeled as pleasant, unpleasant, or neutral depending on whether or not it meets the child's need to feel safe and loved.

Your belief system is largely unconscious and unexamined. Your stories are your survival mechanism. They arise in response to your belief system whose patterns of thought have likely been in place since your childhood. By adulthood, these stories and their underlying patterns can sometimes do more harm than good by distancing you from the reality of the experience itself.

It can be a difficult practice to regularly examine your thoughts and belief system and the stories that they have to tell you about your experiences, but it's worth it. A lot of the really scary things that your stories have to say are simply not true and never come to pass. If you can teach yourself to recognize that fact in the middle of a stressful event, you'll be in a better position to act instead of simply reacting.

## Practice

In the last chapter you practiced observing your thoughts on a daily basis and in response to a predetermined daily cue. Now I'd like you to add to that practice the following suggestions:

1. Observe your mind whenever you're upset. *What's your mind saying?* Try to identify the original thought that came into your mind and then see if you can recognize the story that came after. Ask yourself, *"What's the fact?"* and then *"What's the story?"* Ultimately, this may just be you stating, *"Fact... Story..."* Write it down if that helps you to figure it out or makes it clearer for you.

2. Observe your mind whenever you're happy. *What's your mind saying now?* Try to identify the original thought that came into your mind and then make a note of the story that came after.

3. Whenever you go outside, try to really experience the sensations of nature such as the wind blowing, the sound of thunder, or the feel of the rain. Listen to the sounds around you such as traffic, construction noise, voices, or bird song. See how your mind labels these experiences. Then try to refocus on the pure sensation that you're experiencing and enjoy it for what it is. See if you can separate sensation from story.

4. Sit in a park, or mall, or wherever people pass by and simply observe the story your mind tells about each passing

individual. Even though you don't know these people, your mind has created a judgment about them.

You're teaching yourself to recognize your belief system in action and that's always the first step in de-stressing. You're on your way!

## Summary

- You create stories around internal and external sensations.
- You react to situations in your life based on the stories around the event rather than the event itself.
- Your stories are changeable.
- Your stories are your own unique personal patterns of thought.
- Your stories are based on beliefs you learned from your parents, society, friends and role models.
- Many of these beliefs were first established in your childhood.
- These stories are often unconscious.
- Your stories distance you from the original actual experience and are not necessarily true.

# 4

## The Emotional Consequences of Thought

### You Feel What You Think!

YOU'RE CONSTANTLY EXPERIENCING EMOTIONS. Often they go unrecognized. Have you ever wondered where emotions come from and what their purpose might be?

There are many human emotions but the five most universally recognized are happiness, sadness, fear, anger and disgust. A common theory about emotions goes something like this. You're constantly being exposed to internal and external sensations. These sensations consist of things you see, hear, taste, touch, smell, as well as think. Your brain receives these sensations, identifies them and then decides whether or not they are important to your survival.

Emotions are labels your brain assigns to thoughts and physical sensations. These labels help to inform you as to whether what you are experiencing is perceived to be beneficial, or detrimental, based on your established belief system. In other words, your emotions are a survival mechanism.

Close your eyes and think of a recent unpleasant event that occurred. What are the emotions that arise in response to the thought?

Now think of a pleasant event. Again, what are the emotions that arise in response to the thought?

You're probably beginning to see how powerful your mind is as it creates the constant array of emotions that you experience throughout the day. Your important take-away from this is simply that *your feelings are a consequence of your thoughts!*

## Practice

1. When an emotion arises simply note it in your mind, for example, sadness, anger, happiness, etc.
2. When you notice that you're feeling a certain emotion, see if you can figure out what the original thought, or sensation, was that produced the emotion. Then trace the sequence of reactive thoughts that lead to the development of the emotion.

## Summary

- Emotions are labels that your brain places on thoughts and physical sensations, to tell you whether what's being experienced is perceived to be helpful or harmful to your existence.
- Your mind is responsible for the creation of your emotions.

# 5

## The Physical Consequences of Thought

### Do stories arise from your physical sensations?

I'D LIKE YOU TO BRING YOUR ATTENTION to the physical sensations that are constantly arising within your body. I want you to feel the itches, the squeezes or cramps, all the sensations of pressure, the fluttering or burning sensations. I want you to note whether you're hungry, tired, or in pain and if so, where. Just pay attention to your body for a moment.

 Set your timer again for a quick two minutes. Close your eyes and notice your physical sensations.

Your body is alive with activity and there are always multiple sensations that are occurring without you even being aware of them. When you bring your awareness to your body, you can quickly appreciate the constant physical activity that is present.

Normally your brain receives these many superficial and perfectly normal physical sensations and in effect, filters them out so that they don't reach your conscious awareness. In other words, they just don't bother you. However, there are some individuals, like my patient Larry for example, whose filtering mechanisms are not as effective, or who have a heightened awareness of normal or mildly abnormal sensations and may be extra-aware of them on a regular basis. This is known as *hypervigilance* and often leads to anxiety and exhaustion.

Completely normal sensations encourage Larry to believe that there is something physically wrong with him. His interpretation of these normal sensations, in other words, the story he tells himself in response to these sensations, gives rise to the emotion of anxiety. The anxiety in turn, encourages Larry to focus even more on the physical sensations, thereby providing additional causes for concern. Larry often gets caught in this loop of his own making without even knowing it, but the end result is genuine physical harm resulting from the ongoing stress and anxiety.

Often, you create stories from the physical sensations you experience. As I mentioned earlier, my patient Mika has Irritable Bowel Syndrome, which is a functional gastrointestinal disorder. In response to the abdominal pain, Mika believed that she had bowel cancer at first, which is another example of thinking of the worst possible outcome! Naturally, her stress levels went through the roof in response to this thought, which then further aggravated her condition. When she finally came in to see me she was quite convinced that she was on her deathbed and it took a lot of reassurance to persuade her that she was not.

Frequently, people with chest pain may believe that they're having a heart attack. People with mild headaches may believe that they're having a stroke. All of these stories create emotional responses. People don't just experience physical sensations. They usually experience sensations through the filters of their own reactive stories and emotions. These stories and their accompanying emotions can be more painful than the original physical sensation itself!

Here's another adventure.

Set your timer for a two-minute peak into your mind. Close your eyes and focus on the physical sensations arising in your body once again. This time, see if there are any stories emerging about, or from, the sensations that you're experiencing. Are there any thoughts of anxiety, curiosity or concern that develop because of the sensations? Return to the book when you're done.

Can you recall any previous events where you had some troubling concerns over a physical sensation that you were experiencing? Were you worried that there was something medically serious going on?

So now you've seen that physical sensations can trigger your own story production line to kick into gear, which can then trigger your emotions. Now I'd like to re-examine the idea, presented in chapter one, that your body also responds to thoughts and emotions by producing physical sensations.

## Do physical sensations arise from your thoughts?

Dr. Hans Selyé, a pioneering researcher in the field of biological stress, was instrumental in defining something he called the "stress response." This response demonstrates how there is an intimate connection between the mind and the body.

Your body responds to a perceived threat by initiating a series of physiological events that researchers call an *alarm reaction*. This is your body's first step in dealing with something that your mind tells you is dangerous. Your brain activates a specific branch of your nervous system, called the sympathetic nervous system, which in turn causes your hypothalamus and pituitary glands to release certain substances. These substances stimulate the adrenal glands to release adrenalin and cortisol. Both adrenalin and cortisol race through your body to prepare you to either fight or run away.

This "fight or flight response" results in your heart beating faster, your blood vessels constricting causing your blood pressure to go up, your lungs expanding, your pupils dilating, and your muscles energizing. You're instantly more alert. Once the perceived threat is over your body returns to normal.

However, with chronic stress, that is to say if you think the danger never seems to go away and there is always one threat or another, your body enters a *Stage of Resistance*. Your body starts to adapt to the chronic stress by increasing the production of several hormones such as cortisol, growth hormone, aldosterone and thyroid hormone.

These hormones begin to use up your energy reserves, keeping you on alert.

Real problems occur when your body can't keep it all up any more and you enter the *Stage of Exhaustion*. In this stage, you start to experience long-lasting injuries to multiple organs. The chronic overdrive of hormones leads to depression, diabetes, rheumatoid arthritis, heart disease, cancer, gastrointestinal disease, headache, sleep disorders, an increased risk of infection, and muscle wasting with fatigue. The Stress Response that was initially your mind's attempt at dealing with perceived danger, when left unchecked, ultimately causes chronic injury. Chronic stress can really hurt your body!

There is a definite, intimate connection between your mind and your body. I see this relationship all the time in my office. Patients come to see me with physical complaints. When I inquire as to whether or not there was anything different that was going on in their lives prior to the onset of their symptoms there is a very common response. They say that they were experiencing increased stress.

The stress might be from family, relationships, work, or financial issues. However, people often fail to draw a connection between their stress and their physical illnesses. When you understand that stress can cause real physical symptoms you can begin to direct your problem-solving energy toward the true cause of a problem. An important question to ask yourself if you're experiencing physical symptoms is simply, "Could stress be part of this?"

Larry, as I mentioned before, has Crohn's disease, and that means his own immune system attacks his small and/or large bowel and it becomes inflamed. He has to watch his diet, get enough sleep and generally do everything he can to take care of himself or his Crohn's flares up. When he's under too much stress, he gets headaches and stomach troubles at first. If he paid enough attention, he could work on his stress when these early warning bells told him to. If he doesn't listen, often his Crohn's disease is the next thing to act up and he pays the price.

My patient Mika first noticed her stress when she couldn't sleep very well. Some nights she couldn't get to sleep, others, she'd wake up after only a few hours and watch the time tick by through the night. Mika and her worries weren't getting much rest. Her mother had contacted her from Thailand to say that her sister was very sick and needed expensive treatments. Mika, already supporting the family, tried to take on an additional part-time job but there were not enough hours in the day and the extra work began to take a toll on her marriage. Relationship conflicts became more frequent and she noticed that she was tired all the time. By the time her diarrhea started, she had been living under extreme stress for months.

Now back to you. Try this experiment. Think of a recent situation that was very stressful. As you start to think about it, allow yourself to feel the sensations in your body. What's happening to your breathing? Is it shallow? Deep? Or does it stop at times? Are you sweating? Is your heart beating faster? Do you have scrunched up shoulders, or clenched fists? Are you frowning? Is your stomach in a knot?

 Set your timer for two minutes. Close your eyes to focus and notice if there are any physical sensations in response to a stressful memory. Return to the book right after your two minutes are up. You don't want to dwell in *stress-ville* any longer than you have to!

The physical changes that you can see on the outside in terms of body posture, expression and tension are paralleled by changes that you can't see on the inside of your body.

Next think about a situation that gave you great pleasure. Where do you feel the sensation in your body? What's its nature? What's happening to your breath? Does your body feel tight or relaxed?

 Set your timer for the usual two-minute exploration. Close your eyes and notice if there are any physical sensations in response to a pleasant memory.

We all have our own unique ways of expressing stress in our bodies. For some it can be a racing heart, sweating, headache, back spasm, restlessness, abdominal cramping, or diarrhea. What's your characteristic physical pattern of dealing with stress? Take a moment to write down some of the things you notice about your body when you're stressed.

Chronic stress can be deadly. There is a definite mind-body connection. *Your thoughts can lead to stress and physical consequences.* A more relaxed body can quiet your mind and of course a more relaxed mind can make you feel better. It's encouraging to know that you can break the cycle of thoughts → stress → physical problems by learning how to better deal with your stress and turn off its damaging cascade of hormones. When you recognize the damaging effects of stress on your body, hopefully it will be motivating for you to genuinely commit to learning and practicing the stress-reduction techniques presented throughout the book.

## Practice

1. When you become aware of a physical sensation, take a moment and try to focus your attention on it. Allow yourself to fully experience it.
2. Try to identify any stories arising in response to the sensation.
3. Try to identify if there was a story or emotion present just prior to the physical sensation.

## Summary

- Your body is constantly alive with sensations.
- Thoughts and emotions produce physical sensations.
- Physical sensations also lead to thoughts and emotions.
- There is a mind-body connection and recognizing your own symptoms of stress early will help you avoid its physical consequences.
- Less stress = Less pain!
- A calm mind leads to a calm body. A calm body leads to a calm mind.

# 6
# Mindfulness:
# A Technique to Deal with Stress

**Y**OU'VE ALREADY LEARNED THAT UNDERSTANDING the nature of your mind will help you to relieve your stress. In the previous chapters you've discovered that:

- You normally are not aware of many of your thoughts.
- These thoughts are often about the past or the future but not typically about the present moment.
- You create stories about initial sensations based on your belief system.
- The belief system developed from your childhood experiences as a means of maintaining the love and protection of your caregivers.
- Your thoughts are impermanent, and are always coming and going.
- The mind spontaneously creates these thoughts.
- Thoughts lead to emotional consequences.
- Thoughts lead to physical consequences.
- There is a definite *mind-body connection*.
- Stress is *harmful*!

Having a good understanding of your own mind and stress-response is a great start, but there are many additional ways of trying to deal with stress. Some may work better for you than others. Everyone will have his or her own personal preference. Try to experiment with each technique and see what works best for you. I promise you that every little bit of stress relief helps! In this chapter, I'm going to outline the technique of *mindfulness*, which you can use to reduce your day-to-day stress.

## *What is mindfulness?*

Mindfulness is the act of keeping in mind what you're currently experiencing. It's an accepting, non-judgmental and compassionate awareness of what's going on right at this moment in time. When practicing mindfulness, you bring your attention to the present moment without trying to change it. You're simply present to whatever is being experienced. It's an absolutely wonderful break for both your mind and your body to focus on the present moment in this way. You actively observe your own thoughts, feelings and sensations.

You normally identify and react to the thoughts that come up in your conscious mind. You might grab onto a thought and expand it, resist it, or deny it, or simply let it pass by as a neutral sensation. The bottom line is that you get caught up in your own thoughts. Your emotions and your body react accordingly. Often, especially during times of stress, your thoughts are worries about the past as well as worries about what might happen in the future. Your emotions and body are reacting as if it's all occurring in the here and now. The present becomes the best place to give you a break.

Mindfulness is not just being aware of what's present. It also gives you more insight into how your mind works. This allows you to change the way you relate to your mental, emotional and physical experiences. By mentally creating a bit of breathing space, you don't have to unconsciously react to whatever arises and you can experience the events in your life from a place of greater clarity and wisdom. By practicing the techniques of mindfulness, you'll be better able to consciously respond to situations and you will not just automatically react to things in accordance with the long established patterns of your belief system.

In this and subsequent chapters, you'll learn to be present only to what's happening in this very moment. You'll be better able to understand your own conditioned patterns. You'll be less powerless in the face of the chain of events that links thoughts, to stories, to emotions, to body sensations, to reactions. The practice of mindfulness is a wonderfully liberating process that can free you from the tyranny of your own mind. There is inherent wisdom, peace, understanding, empathy and compassion that reside within the silence of awareness and acceptance.

Think about whether you have ever personally experienced any of the following scenarios:

- Have you ever reacted to a thought with a sudden, extreme, uncontrolled emotional response?
- Do you experience repetitive thoughts that just won't go away and do you feel very agitated by them?
- Does it feel at times that you have no control over your mind?
- Does your mind seem like it never turns off? Is it very difficult to fall asleep because of all the mental activity?
- Have you ever said something and then regretted it as soon as you said it?
- Have you ever been either happy or sad and heard some news that instantly changed your mood?

These are the types of thought activity that you'll experience without the clarity that mindfulness brings. Your mind is simply reacting to every sensation that comes its way.

## Mindfulness and Awareness

The first important step in the practice of mindfulness is to intentionally be aware (i.e., mindful) of your thoughts, emotions and physical sensations as they pop up. You've already been practicing a version of this in some of the previous exercises that I've asked you to try. Without this awareness, you're not conscious of the multiple sensations that are driving your behaviour. You're just swept along in the tidal wave of anger, sadness, judgment, happiness or whatever strong sensation arises. With mindfulness you can start to break this unconscious chain of reactions.

You are aware of what comes into your conscious mind to some degree. The problem is that you immediately identify with the thought, emotion, or physical sensation that arises. Mindfulness involves being aware of what you are aware of. There is a knowing that anger, fear, sadness etc., is present. This gives you space to respond, rather than react, to what arises.

Mindfulness helps you to begin to recognize that you're constantly being exposed to multiple sensations but are often unaware of them and how they may be influencing you. It's an excellent alternative to allowing yourself to be absorbed in your own thoughts. You can bring a greater awareness to all of the realms of your experience. You can bring awareness to what you're thinking, what you're feeling and what you're physically experiencing in the present moment.

It's as if your mind is a log being carried along a river. The log moves according to the flow of the river, being pushed and pulled depending on the water flow. However, with mindfulness you're now a boat on the river. You can experience the flow of the river but you're separate from it and you have the ability to control your movements as well.

Give it a try. This next exercise will help you learn to become aware of what you're experiencing on a continual basis. Be open to whatever sensation arises. It could be a thought, sound, smell or physical sensation. If a thought appears, the moment you recognize it, just say, "*thinking*" to yourself. It doesn't have to be out loud, just in your mind will do! If you become aware of an emotion just say, "*feeling*." If your arm itches, or your neck hurts, or some other physical sensation comes to your attention, just say something like, "*body sensation*" to yourself.

 Go ahead and set your timer for two minutes. Close your eyes, notice your sensations and as you do, name them as "*thinking*," "*feeling*," or "*body sensation*." Return to the book when you're through.

This exercise is a way of cultivating your awareness but at the same time distancing yourself from the meaning that you would normally attach to your thoughts and feelings. If you get carried away for a moment and lost in thought, don't worry about it! It's absolutely normal for that to happen. Just acknowledge this by saying, "*thinking*" and return to monitoring and labeling your experiences.

What normally happens is that when an emotion such as anger, sadness, suffering, or joy arises, there is no awareness about what's happening. You just get swept away by the emotion. You may not even be consciously aware that a particular emotion is even present. You identify so strongly with the emotion that you become the emotional state itself, instead of recognizing that it's just a state of mind that has arisen.

There are many levels to what you experience in any given moment. It's important to be aware of *why* a particular thought or emotion has arisen. For example, if you're angry, this could actually reflect an underlying fear that you have, which is, in turn, based on previous experiences. We will explore the origins of some of these underlying forces later in the book.

## Mindfulness and Labeling

It's time for another exercise. Remember that this book is actually about you. This time, when a thought, feeling or physical sensation pops up, I want you to go a bit further with your labeling and actually try to name the experience. You're trying to become more specific about each experience, rather than just generically noting the labels: "*thinking*," "*feeling*," and "*body sensation*." This time, mentally say something like: "*judging*," "*criticizing*," "*sadness*," "*happiness*," "*throbbing sensation*," or "*stabbing sensation*." You get the idea.

Set your timer for two minutes. Close your eyes, notice your sensations and label them specifically, and then return to the text.

You've just brought mindful awareness to your experience. Your mind was too busy noticing itself and your body to be engaged in the, often artificial, manufacture of stressful thoughts. You just gave yourself a bit of a break. Way to go!

## Short Circuiting Judgments and Encouraging Acceptance

With mindfulness, the goal is to take note of an experience for what it is without any further judgment and without the need to change what's happening. Ideally there's no layering over the experience with further, personal, biased perspectives. These biased perspectives lead to either a desire for, or a rejection of, what you're currently experiencing. Remember that your normal response to an experience is to have an initial judgment of the event. Rather than just accepting this reaction, you tend to amplify it and judge yourself even further.

When Mika's on a diet and has some ice cream, she feels bad that she gave in to her cravings. She's angry about what she's done. Next, she makes the judgment that she's always making these mistakes, and her pattern of thoughts leads right into her habitual story about how she's hopeless and so fat that no one could ever love her. All this from a bowl of ice cream!

Ideally there would just be the awareness that she has eaten ice cream without the subsequent judgments. She would then accept that she chose to eat ice cream without any denial, guilt, or resistance. This may not have been the best decision that she could have made given her diet, but she doesn't have to torment herself over it. She can accept and learn from what she has done and act accordingly in the future.

However, as you now know, it is the nature of the mind to compare every event to a personal belief system. If Mika could bring mindfulness to her situation, she would be aware of the mental, emotional, and physical responses and just accept the judgment and anger without needing to deny it or to be totally swept away by it.

It requires a lot of mental energy to either suppress an event or actively seek after it. In fact, when you actively try to suppress a mental state, it usually gives it more energy to return and persevere. Inevitably, further automatic judgments develop. Mindfulness can help you to simply be aware, that is to stay present, to the anger, frustration, or hopelessness that may arise as a consequence of a decision, without encouraging these emotions any further.

## Mindfulness and Equanimity

Equanimity is another feature of mindfulness. When you're present in the moment to what you're experiencing, you're calm and accepting. Equanimity means basically that you accept things as they are. You may not like what you're experiencing, but how can you change what has already happened? It is what it is!

The action of eating ice cream may not have been Mika's best choice under the circumstances, but this doesn't make her unlovable! The action may not have been the best decision, but it doesn't make her a bad person either. The practice of mindfulness stops habitual thought patterns in their tracks whenever you choose to apply it. You'll practice just accepting whatever arises, whether it's the initial event, or the automatic judgments that sneak in before you can refocus your awareness again on the present.

## Non-Attachment and Non-Identification: Letting Go of the Velcro Mind

When you say to yourself, "I am angry," or "I am hurt," or "I am sad," you're personalizing your experience. You're identifying with the "I" that you perceive is experiencing this emotion. This serves to make it feel more believable, more real and more powerful. If you can learn to describe your emotions with the phrases "*now* anger," "*now* pain," "*now* sadness," you're distancing yourself by just labeling a generic mental state, an emotion, or a physical sensation. In a way, you're gaining some much-needed perspective, so that you can stand back a bit.

Recall that thoughts pop up and vanish just as quickly, but when you latch on to them and stick them into a pattern of storytelling, emotions are triggered. It's all invented, imagined and constructed in your Velcro Mind. The mind likes to attach new experiences to memories of previous ones and to personally identify with what's occurring. If you can start to take the "I" out of things, you will be practicing what mindfulness describes as non-identification and non-attachment. Think of an emotion that you experience as not 'your' emotion per se but just as 'an emotion', a mental state that has developed and can just as easily go away. It's just how your mind works.

It's important to recognize that the term is non-attachment, not detachment. You're not walling yourself off from the experience in any way. The experience just becomes a little less sticky and your Velcro Mind, which likes to grab and hold onto things, can let go a bit. You're just recognizing an experience for its true, impermanent nature and labeling it. In actual fact, by doing so, you're really experiencing the mental state and its emotional and physical expression in its totality.

## You As the Observer:
### *What to do? Don't do anything!*

When being mindful, you're an observer in your own mind and body. This may be the most difficult thing mindfulness asks you to do, but the best way to think about it is that you're really not doing anything. You're just being present to what presents itself without reacting, judging or criticizing. Can you just observe what's unfolding?

On the one hand, it's a passive process in that you're not trying to alter your experiences in any way. It can also be a very active personal process, as it initially requires a lot of strength, courage and endurance to allow very strong thoughts, feelings and physical sensations to just be present without wanting to change them and without getting swept up in their drama. It can also be very interesting to see how dynamic and changing any sensation can be as you simply observe it.

When you're able to observe your mind's own actions from a distance, by just focusing your awareness, this creates a separation from the activities of the mind. This is the much-needed 'step back' that we talked about earlier. You become the witness, the observer to the experience rather than the "I" who is experiencing the event. You can then come to the moment with curiosity, interest and acceptance. Awareness is very valuable, as it allows you to be present from a place that is not your usual thinking, evaluating, judging mind. By observing your thoughts and stepping back, you realize that who you are, is more than just the sum of your thoughts.

## Mindfulness and Compassion: Be Kind to Yourself

Compassion is an integral part of mindfulness. When you're present to the wild thoughts, emotions and physical sensations that your mind and body are throwing at you every second of every day, it's important to recognize that all this simply reflects your own unique makeup. What makes you uniquely you, is significantly influenced by your inner child and its need to be loved and accepted. The inner child is a part of your mind that still reacts to events in a child-like manner.

There is only one you. Have compassion for the child you once were and the difficulties inherent in the human condition. Have compassion and understanding for yourself, as you go through a process of trying to change long-standing patterns and deeply held beliefs by observing them with your newfound knowledge and awareness. You need to accept, as best you can, your own humanity and cherish who you are. You do not deserve to be rejected and criticized (especially by your own judging mind!) but you do deserve to be honored and loved.

## Mindfulness and Letting Go: Don't Ride the Train!

When something happens that you feel strongly about, you probably cling to the story and thoughts surrounding the event. You identify with the event and embellish it. This feeds the event and along with its accompanying storyline and emotions, it has more energy to remain front and center in your awareness. It's important for you to try to experience something only as long as it naturally persists without prolonging it with amplification, attachment and identification. There is a constant train of thoughts that you're receiving. You have the choice of riding on the train and letting it take you wherever it goes, or stepping off the train and just watching it go by without ever climbing on board.

## Mindfulness and the Origin of Thought

We previously examined the origin of thoughts. We discussed the fact that the mind measures every internal and external sensation against a conditioned belief system in order to determine whether the sensation is valuable or not. Your belief system primarily originated back when you were a child. You internalized your parents' standards and acted accordingly, in order to feel safe, loved and protected. The fear of abandonment is one of the prime motivators of a child's actions.

The child creates a story in response to every new sensation, which leads to an unconscious, conditioned, habitual response pattern. This is the foundation of your belief system. If you can consciously recognize this, then you will be better able to appreciate the fact that, as an adult, some of your responses are actually controlled by the belief system of a four-year-old child; the child that you once were!

This may have been a very effective belief system and response pattern for you when you were four but that was many years ago. Your thoughts should seem a little less powerful and meaningful as you consider that their origins may be your early childhood.

# Mindfulness and the Emptiness of Thought

Mindfulness is not just about cultivating an awareness of the present moment. It's important to also see the true nature of your experiences. You are often so caught up in the content of your experiences that you believe them to be real, rather than an interpretation created by your busy mind. You can't let go of what your mind is creating, its stories and drama, and so you strongly identify with this interpretation as being who you are.

Think about the following questions briefly to help you better realize that your thoughts are temporary and illusory: Can you see a thought? Can you feel a thought? Can you point to a thought? Do you think a thought or does it arise spontaneously? Can you find the "I" who thinks a thought? Review the practice and summary sections of chapter 3 to reconnect with the idea that your mind is quite the storyteller and that your thoughts are not the whole truth.

As we progress in this book, I will outline additional techniques that will demonstrate how your mind creates its sense of reality and from that, its sense of suffering as well. In examining the process of thought development, from initial experience to story-creation and subsequent emotional and physical responses, you will see how the mind takes every experience and changes it according to your belief system. One such technique involves having a conversation, or dialogue, with your inner critic. You will see that the origin of your belief system is your own inner child trying to be safe.

When you can see how your thoughts are your own mental creations, empty illusions and fabrications, you'll have the key that will allow you to let these thoughts go. This key is nothing more than a clear understanding of the process of thought development. It will give you the tools to see through the smoke of your conditioned experiences and realize an underlying truth; each thought is basically empty. This is what's so liberating about mindfulness.

## Mindfulness and Impermanence

A thought, emotion or physical sensation doesn't last forever. When you're in a certain frame of mind it sure feels permanent and you probably believe that it is. However, if you really observe whatever you're experiencing, you'll see it change. You may have some truly terrible thoughts about yourself or something that happened to you, but ultimately your mind lets go of it all. You then, at least temporarily, start thinking about what you're going to have for dinner, what to wear tomorrow or what shopping you have to do.

If you can get your mind around the idea that *all* mental states are temporary and impermanent, it can give you the courage to face what life is throwing at you. Be comforted by the knowledge that however bad it may appear, it will change in time. Remember that thoughts are like clouds in the sky that come and go across your field of consciousness.

## Mindfulness and the Light of Awareness

It's very interesting to observe what happens to any sensation when mindfulness is brought to it. When a sensation is observed, it changes. Just think about doing something like singing, playing sports, or talking in public. How does it feel when you know that someone is watching? How does it change the action? When you bring a mindful awareness to your sensations, it has the same effect.

It's time for another exercise. Think about something that has given you some difficulty recently. When the story arises, begin to label the emotions that pop up, just as you practiced earlier. Say things such as "Now sadness," "Now anger," "Now pain". Bring your attention to what you're experiencing. Just be the observer. Don't start thinking about it! Simply observe what happens to the story or emotion. Be curious. How does it change? Does it become stronger or weaker? Does the emotion keep growing or quiet down? Does the story continue or stop?

Set your timer for two minutes, close your eyes, notice what happens to a difficult memory as you observe it and then read on.

It's fascinating to observe the power that mindfulness can have over your sensations. When your mind is watched, it seems to know that and it changes its behaviour. When you bring mindfulness to your sensations, it decreases their intensity. They often stop altogether.

Mindfulness is a technique that I personally have found to be a liberating experience. I'm no longer always at the mercy of my mind and the stories it tells. I have the ability to respond appropriately rather than reacting unconsciously to what arises. It truly is a path to a peaceful mind!

## Practice

There are several things you can do everyday to start practicing mindfulness:

1. For five to ten minutes in the morning and/or in the evening, sit quietly and simply observe the thoughts, emotions and physical sensations that arise. Label them as you notice them e.g., "Now thinking," "Now sadness," "Now a squeezing discomfort," etc.

2. When a negative, or unpleasant event occurs, stop and observe the thoughts, emotions and physical sensations that arise as a consequence of the event.

3. When a happy, or pleasant event occurs, stop and observe the thoughts, emotions and physical sensations that arise as a result of the event.

4. During the day, whenever you can, try to label whatever internal or external sensation comes into your consciousness.

5. Choose an environmental cue that will help you to be mindful. This could be, for example, before you eat, brush your teeth,

shave, shower, take a walk, or answer the phone. Set your wristwatch or cell phone so that an alarm goes off every hour. Whenever a cue occurs, stop and try to be mindful of what you're thinking, feeling and physically experiencing at that moment.

6. Put *Post-it* notes up around the house, in your car, or at your place of work to remind you to be mindful.

## Summary

- You constantly identify with your thoughts and emotions.
- Mindfulness is an accepting, non-judging, non-attached and compassionate awareness of your experience as it unfolds in the present moment.
- Mindfulness is the cultivated ability to be present to what you experience without having to react to it or change it.
- Mindfulness encourages you to be intentionally aware of your thoughts, emotions and physical sensations whenever possible.
- Mindfulness encourages you to accept them as mental energy that arises and then as quickly moves on.
- Be an observer in your own mind and body and try not to identify so strongly with your thoughts and emotions.
- Practicing more compassion for yourself is an important aspect of mindfulness.
- By mindfully focusing on what occurs in your body during emotional responses, you can learn how to calm yourself sooner.
- Thoughts, emotions and physical sensations don't last forever and will change or go away. Just be patient.

# 7

## Mindfulness and the Breath

**D**O YOU HAVE STRESS THAT MAKES IT DIFFICULT to enjoy your life? Have you found a simple way to deal with it that makes you feel better? Wouldn't it be great if you had the means to deal with your stress that was always available, didn't cost a thing, you could learn very quickly and that worked? This is not a fantasy. The answer is your breath.

There is a definite connection between your breathing and your mental state. Whatever happens in your mind influences your breathing and vice versa...how you breathe affects how you feel. When you're in a stressful situation you likely contract your muscles, which then restrict your breathing. You may also become so focused on a problem that you may even forget to breathe at all and actually temporarily hold your breath. This can deprive your entire body of oxygen, so your stress-induced tension negatively affects your body down to the last cell.

These are just the short-term effects of stress on your body, but over the long term, the muscles around your blood vessels can become so contracted that they can even lead to high blood pressure and heart disease. Poor breathing can lead to many additional physical problems. When your breath is calm and deep this tends to relax your mind and body. It's really that simple! Therefore, one of the most important tools for managing stress is learning to regulate your breath.

The most exciting thing about learning to monitor and control your breathing is that it's a method of stress reduction that's there for you to use in any situation...and it works! Breathing is the key to calming your mind and relaxing your body.

We all know how to breathe and thank goodness it carries on all day and night without any conscious

55

control. However, just because you breathe automatically, doesn't mean that you're doing it in the most effective way and enjoying all of its benefits. You may have developed some unhealthy habits that you're probably not even aware of, such as shallow and irregular breathing with jerks and pauses.

There are four steps to achieving better breathing. I call these steps the **ABCDE** of breathing.

- **A**wareness
- **B**reathe **C**almly
- **D**iaphragm
- **E**xhalation

Awareness of the breath trains you to watch your breath. Breathing calmly, from the diaphragm and with a prolonged exhalation is a conscious technique to retrain your breathing so that you'll ultimately develop the habit of breathing automatically in a way that leads, most effectively, to stress reduction.

The following 4-step program will guide you through everything you need to know to begin breathing better. A series of four sections and associated exercises outline how you can become aware of your breath and use it to control your stress. Practice each of the major sections until you feel comfortable with it. Each section and its accompanying exercises, builds on the section before, so please be patient and do each section's exercises before moving on.

## Step 1: Awareness

In this first step, all that's really involved is bringing your *awareness to your breath*. Because you breathe automatically, you don't normally think about breathing. This is an opportunity to become more aware of the nature of your breath. As you become aware of your breathing, don't try to consciously change it. Having an awareness of your breath and an acceptance of how it is without trying to change it is a perfect example of mindfulness in action.

Let's try this exercise. Just follow your breath. Don't try to change it. When your lungs want to breathe in, allow that to happen. When your lungs want to breathe out, allow that to happen. When you stop breathing in between your exhalation and inhalation that's okay too. Rest in the stillness of the pause. Just observe whatever happens as it happens.

- Notice whether your breath is deep or shallow.
- Is it quiet or loud?
- Is it short or long?
- Is it tight or relaxed?
- Are there pauses in your breathing between breathing in or breathing out?
- Do you feel the act of breathing mostly in your belly, chest, nose, or somewhere else?
- Do your in-breath and out-breath take the same amount of time?

Become curious!

 Now that you have some idea of what you'll be observing as you notice your own breathing patterns, set your timer for two minutes, close your eyes, be aware of your breath and come back to the book when you're done.

What did you happen to notice about your breathing? Is every breath different?

The next interesting aspect of breathing that you'll notice is what happens to the nature, rhythm, and ease of the breath as you continue to observe it.

Try it now.

 Set your timer for the usual two minutes and close your eyes. Observe what happens to your breathing as you bring your attention to it. Continue reading when you've completed this exercise.

Did your breath change as you watched it? Did it become more even, smooth and relaxed? You will find that, as you bring the practice of mindfulness to your breath, it does change, just because it knows you're watching it. Simply bringing your attention to your breath will usually change the nature and rhythm of your breathing without you having to do anything else.

Breathing that is irregular and shallow will become more even and deep. An even breath will lead to a greater state of physical and mental relaxation. If you have a calmer breathing pattern, you'll have a more relaxed mind, which is less likely to overreact to whatever is going on around you. When you are upset your breathing can become even more shallow and uneven.

Bringing your awareness to your breathing can also give you a clue as to what sort of mental or physical state you may be in.

Breath-awareness also has the added advantage of putting you in touch with the present moment. This can give you a break from all the worrying that your mind likes to do about your memories of the past and your fantasies of the future. You're less likely to get caught up in all the endless thinking and worrying if your attention is exclusively on your breathing. There is no room for other thoughts.

You'll find that it can sometimes be difficult for you to completely surrender to the movement of the breath without trying to control it. This 'letting go' is a key aspect of breath-awareness. You can experience this sense of surrender if you take a deep breath in and then emphasize breathing out until there is no more breath left. Then you would rest in the prolonged pause between the exhalation and inhalation until your body automatically wanted to start breathing again. It's unnecessary to try to control the breathing process at that point. You're still simply observing your experience of the automatic movements of breathing.

Any moment, any second, that you do pay attention to your breath, you're taking a huge step toward dealing with stress. The most important point is to remember to be *aware of your breath as often as you can*. Continuity of practice is essential. A calm breath leads to a calm mind.

The following are helpful exercises that you can do over the next week to develop your breath-awareness.

1. For approximately ten minutes in the morning and/or ten minutes in the evening, sit in a chair, relax and observe your breath with your eyes closed.

2. Initially count your breaths, as counting can help you to remain focused on your breathing. An in and out breath counts as one cycle. Breathe in and out and count one, then in and out and count two, etc. Do this up to ten and then count backwards from ten to one. Keep repeating this cycle as long as you find it helpful.

3. You can use a timer with an alarm to let you know when your ten minutes are up. This way you won't become distracted as you focus on how much time you have been practicing, and it can help prolong your practice should you become restless or bored before your scheduled time is up.

4. Throughout the day, use normal daily activities or times to remind you to bring your awareness to your breath. For example, pay attention to your breathing before each meal, whenever you hang up the phone, before you go for a walk, when you're stopped at a red light, whenever you get on the bus or train, during television commercials, or even after a visit to the washroom. Make a plan that works for you and write it down. It's all up to you to think of what events in your day you can use to remind yourself to spend a few moments focusing on your breathing.

5. You can put *Post-it* notes in different locations around your house, or place of work, that perhaps simply say "*breathe*," as a reminder to yourself to do a little breath watching.

6. Another helpful trick is to set the alarm on your watch or cell phone for every two to three hours to remind you to bring your attention to your breath.

7. Try to follow your breathing for a minimum of five breaths when you see one of your reminders. Counting your breaths helps to keep you focused.

8. When you're under stress, bring your attention to your breathing. Count your breaths and continue to watch your breathing until the stress fades.

9. The more you practice breath-awareness, the more it becomes a regular habit.

## Step 2: Breathe Calmly

In the last section, you observed that, as your breathing became smoother, deeper and more even, you felt more relaxed. The breath is unique in that it's under both unconscious and conscious control. When you get upset, your breathing becomes irregular and shallow and you may even hold your breath. However, you can consciously control your breathing so as to duplicate the type of breathing that will bring about a state of calmness. Remember, relaxation is only a breath away!

Instead of just observing your breathing, you're going to try to gently change it and make it calmer. Consciously deepening your breathing will make use of your entire lung area, keep your chest muscles active, reduce stale, trapped air in the lungs and allow you to inhale more fresh air. You're going to be practicing breath exercises that will start to re-train your body to breathe healthier.

Try this exercise. Follow your breath but this time I want you to consciously try to alter it.

- Try to make your breathing *smooth, quiet, soft and deep.*
- Your *in and out-breaths* should be smoothly joined, with no pause in between them. Try to see your breathing as one continuous, smooth, flowing movement.
- Breathe in and out through your *nose*, if you can, rather than through your mouth. You may need to keep your mouth closed in order to re-route your breath through your nose. Your nostrils purify and warm your breath. They are also a wonderful point to mentally focus on, as you follow the movement of your breath in and out of your body.

- *Straighten your back* as you breathe. If you're bent over, it will be more difficult to have an even, deep, full breath. A bent body position can crowd your lungs, so try to make sure your back is relatively straight but still relaxed.

 Now that you have a better idea of how to consciously breathe calmly, set your timer for two minutes, close your eyes, and give it a try.

How did you feel as you breathed in a calm, even, deep and smooth fashion? As your breathing became calmer did you notice that you were mentally, emotionally and physically beginning to relax?

The following are exercises that you can do to further develop the practice of breathing in a calm and smooth manner:

1. For approximately ten minutes in the morning and/or ten minutes in the evening, sit in a chair, relax and consciously breathe in a calm manner with your eyes closed.
2. Initially count your breaths, as counting can help you to remain focused on your breathing. An in and out-breath counts as one cycle. Breathe in and out and count one, then in and out and count two, etc. Do this up to ten and then count backwards from ten to one. Keep repeating this cycle as long as you find it helpful.
3. You can use a timer with an alarm to let you know when your ten minutes are up.
4. Throughout the day, use normal daily activities or times to remind you to consciously breathe calmly. For example, pay attention to your breathing before each meal, whenever you hang up the phone, before you go for a walk, when you're stopped at a red light, whenever you get on the bus or train, during television commercials, or even after a visit to the washroom. Make a plan that works for you and write it down. It's all up to you to think of what events in your day you can use to remind yourself to spend a few moments focusing on your breathing.

5. You can put *Post-it* notes in different locations around your house, or place of work, that perhaps simply say "*breathe*," as a reminder to yourself to do conscious, calm breathing.

6. Another helpful trick is to set the alarm on your watch or cell phone for every two to three hours to remind you to breathe calmly.

7. Try to follow your breathing for a minimum of five breaths when you see one of your reminders. Counting your breaths helps to keep you focused.

8. When you're under stress, bring your attention to your breathing. Count your breaths and continue to watch your breathing until the stress fades.

9. The more you practice breathing calmly, the more it becomes a regular habit.

## Step 3: Breathing from Your Diaphragm

Welcome to step three of the breathing exercises. You'll look at the **D** of the **ABCDE** of breathing, *diaphragmatic breathing*. The diaphragm is a muscle that separates the chest from the belly or abdominal area. With diaphragmatic breathing, or what's commonly known as *belly breathing*, your abdomen expands, rather than the chest, with each in-breath. The diaphragm muscle moves down and the lungs are allowed more room to open up. Air flows deeply into the lower part of the lungs, which are actually better at taking up oxygen than the upper lungs.

When you are anxious or stressed, tension forms in the chest, neck and belly and you predominantly breathe from your chest. Your breathing becomes shallow, and at times you may even hold your breath without knowing it. If you can consciously learn to use the diaphragm, or belly, to breathe more deeply, you will automatically be breathing in larger amounts of fresh air.

Let's practice. Find a comfortable chair to sit in. Please sit in an upright, relaxed manner with your eyes closed. Wear loose-fitting clothes for this exercise, as tight clothes around the waist will limit your belly's movement.

Start to breathe and put one hand on your chest and the other on your abdomen over your belly button. As you breathe, notice whether it's the hand, which is over your chest, or the hand over your stomach area that is rising. If it's your chest that is rising, consciously try and make your abdomen rise instead. Focus your attention on allowing the belly, instead of the chest, to rise when breathing in and then let your belly fall naturally as you breathe out. Relax your stomach muscles completely during each in-breath.

 Set your timer for two minutes, close your eyes to better concentrate and try to consciously breathe from the diaphragm. When your timer goes off, return to the book.

How did that feel? Diaphragmatic breathing is a fantastic and dependable way to reduce anxiety, encourage relaxation and dissolve stress.

The following is a series of exercises that will help strengthen your ability to breathe from your diaphragm and establish the habit of breathing from your belly instead of your chest. Practice these exercises until you feel comfortable doing them and they feel natural.

1. For approximately ten minutes in the morning and/or ten minutes in the evening sit upright in a relaxed manner in a chair. Alternatively you may lie down on a bed and simply breathe from the diaphragm with your eyes closed. Place one hand over your chest and another on your abdomen to help guide you to breathe from your diaphragm.

2. Count your breaths to remain focused on your breathing.

3. Use a timer with an alarm to let you know when your practice time is up.

4. If you find that your belly won't move out yet your chest continues to, try this: Lie on your back with your knees bent and put a heavy book on your mid-abdomen approximately over the belly button. The book will help to focus your mind

on expanding the abdomen. Focus your attention on allowing the book to rise as you breathe in and fall as you breathe out.

5. Throughout the day, use your normal daily activities or specific times to remind you to breathe from your belly.

6. Put up *Post-it* notes in different locations as a reminder to yourself to emphasize diaphragmatic breathing.

7. Set the alarm on your watch, computer or cell for every two to three hours to remind you to bring your attention to diaphragmatic breathing.

8. Try to follow your breathing for a minimum of five breaths at specified times or whenever you see one of your reminders. Counting your breaths can help keep you focused.

9. When you're under stress bring your attention to your breath and start to consciously breathe in a calm, deep, smooth, even and quiet manner from the diaphragm. Count your breaths and continue breathing from your diaphragm until the stress goes away.

10. The more you practice diaphragmatic breathing the more it becomes a regular habit. A new pattern of deep, smooth, even diaphragmatic breathing will then become the way you normally breathe throughout the day. You really can change how your body and mind respond to stress one breath at a time.

## Step 4: Exhalation

In the final step of your breathing program you are going to look at how *exhalation*, or the act of breathing out, is a very effective tool for promoting mental and physical relaxation.

The autonomic nervous system is the boss of your heart rate, blood pressure, breathing and other bodily functions that, thankfully, carry on without you having to think about them. You can think of autonomic as automatic. You don't have to tell your heart to beat faster when you run, or slow down when you relax. But the autonomic nervous system is always paying attention for you and if you're feeling stressed, even a little bit, it's already getting your body prepared to fight, or run, or do whatever you might need to do. Unfortunately, nowadays, we're pretty much always a little bit stressed. This stress keeps you in a "fight or flight" mode constantly, which is exhausting work for your poor nervous system. It needs a break. That's where the breath comes in.

Your autonomic nervous system is not something you can directly control; your heart beats; you breathe; your digestion carries on without you having to think about any of these activities. However, your breath is under conscious as well as under autonomic control. Your breathing turns out to be the link between you and your autonomic nervous system.

When you inhale, or breathe in, it stimulates the part of your autonomic nervous system, called the sympathetic nervous system, which is responsible for getting you ready for stress. Luckily, when you exhale, or breathe out, it turns on the part of the nervous system called the parasympathetic system, which tells everything to calm down. This provides you with a unique opportunity to help your nervous system relax. If you can make the amount of time that you breathe out longer than the time it takes to breathe in, you're intentionally instructing your autonomic nervous system to relax. It's that easy.

It's time for another exercise. Focus your attention on your breath and simply count approximately how many seconds it takes for you to breathe in and then count how long it takes for you to breathe out. Notice whether or not it takes the same amount of time. You'll probably observe that the time taken to breathe in and the time taken to breathe out is not always equal, and that this pattern changes depending upon your mental state.

Continue counting the time taken to breathe in and out. See if you can consciously prolong the exhalation such that the time it takes to breathe out is longer than the time it takes to breathe in. You may even intentionally try to prolong the exhalation for as long as it feels comfortable.

Set your timer for your usual two minutes. Close your eyes and consciously breathe with a prolonged exhalation (a longer out-breath). When you're finished come back to the book.

How do you feel mentally and physically after a few minutes of prolonging the exhalation of your breath? Is there a greater sense of relaxation?

The following is a series of exercises that will help increase your awareness and usage of the out-breath. Practice these for the next week.

1. For approximately ten minutes in the morning and/or ten minutes in the evening sit upright, in a relaxed manner, in a chair. Keep your eyes closed and simply breathe with a prolonged exhalation. This means that the exhalation, or the act of breathing out, takes longer than the inhalation, or breathing in.
2. Count your breaths to remain focused on your breathing.
3. Use a timer with an alarm to let you know when your practice time is up.
4. Try to extend the exhalation for as long as it feels comfortable.
5. Throughout the day, use normal daily activities as a reminder, or set time cues, to remind you to bring your awareness to your exhalations.
6. Put up *Post-it* notes in different locations as a reminder to yourself to emphasize exhalation.
7. Set the alarm on your watch, computer, or cell phone for every few hours to remind you to bring your attention to your breath.
8. Try to follow your breathing for a minimum of five breaths at specified times, or when you see one of your reminders, just as you did in the previous breathing exercises.
9. When you're under stress bring your attention to your breath and start to consciously breathe in a calm, deep, smooth, even and quiet manner, from the diaphragm, with a prolonged

exhalation. Count your breaths and continue to breathe with a prolonged exhalation until the stress evaporates.

10. The more you practice prolonged-exhalation breathing the more it becomes a regular habit. Your new pattern of breathing will become the way you normally breathe. You're beginning to de-stress, one breath at a time!

## Practice

You've learned that breathing is a highly effective way to reduce mental and physical stress. This is supported by a real physiological connection between a calm breath and a relaxed state.

1. Initially, a formal practice session where you set aside a daily designated time to practice conscious breathing will begin to *retrain* the way you normally breathe. Focus on breathing in a calm manner, from the diaphragm and with a prolonged exhalation. Continue this formal practice until you feel that you automatically breathe in this effective and relaxed way.

2. Try, as often as you can during the day, to bring awareness to your breath *without trying to control it*. This will help train you in the practice of mindfulness, where you're just present to what presents itself without a need to change it. It will also help with mental and physical relaxation.

3. Use environmental cues, *Post-it* notes, and an alarm of some sort, as reminders to support your practice.

4. The real test of the usefulness of breath training is when you encounter a stressful event. Can you remember at those times to use the **ABCDE** of breathing?

5. When you are experiencing a very stressful event you may need to consciously control your breath, breathing in a calm, deep, slow and even manner from the diaphragm with a prolonged exhalation.

6. At stressful times it can also help to count your breaths for as long as it takes to feel more relaxed.

## Summary

- The breath is the key to stress reduction.
- There are four steps to achieving better breathing that I call the **ABCDE** of breathing. These steps are 1. Awareness 2. Breathe Calmly 3. Diaphragm and 4. Exhalation.
- Awareness of the breath trains you to watch your breath without trying to change it. While breathing calmly, from the diaphragm and with a prolonged exhalation is a technique to retrain your breathing to maximize stress relief.
- Focusing on your breath will help to remove you from the intensity of your thoughts.
- The benefits of using the **ABCDE** of breathing will only come when you use this technique regularly. Practice your new breath control exercises as often as you can and your efforts will be rewarded. You can breathe easier knowing you have the tools to help yourself. Relaxation is only a breath away.

# 8

## Mindfulness and the Body

## Your Body Has a Mind of It's Own

D O YOU SPEND SO MUCH TIME in your head that you're disconnected from what's going on in your body? Your body is alive with energy that constantly changes and your physical sensations are intimately related to your thoughts and emotions. When you're emotionally upset this is reflected in your body.

Remember the Stress Response? Your mind is constantly trying to keep you safe and when your mind perceives a threat, it sends out a message that leads to the release of adrenalin and cortisol. Recall that these powerful hormones prepare you for a flight or fight response. Your heart rate increases, your blood vessels constrict and you sweat. Your muscles prepare for action and the pupils of your eyes open wide.

Unfortunately, with chronic stress the persistent release of these hormones causes your body organs to be damaged leading to all kinds of nasty health problems and diseases. You're probably starting to see how important it is to maintain a state of mindfulness regarding your physical sensations and to actively create relaxation in your body in order to overcome the harmful effects of stress. There's a direct connection between your body and your mind. If you relax your body, your mind relaxes and vice versa.

When you're emotionally upset, how is this reflected in your body for you personally? Do you experience shallow breathing, diarrhea, sweating, your heart pounding, headaches, tension in your jaw or shoulders? Do you have "butterflies" in your stomach? Are you

normally aware of the physical sensations you have in response to stressful thoughts and emotions? As you begin to concentrate on what your body's feeling, you'll find that your muscles automatically begin to release some of their tension.

You've also learned that your thoughts are very powerful things and that it's easy to identify with them and get carried away. By bringing your attention to the physical expression of your thoughts and emotions, the experience is more distant and 'selfless'. You can step out of the storyline. You now have another option for how you experience your thoughts and emotions. You can experience them more as a sensation rather than identifying with them by using the very personal "I", as in, "I am angry" or "I am sad."

Thoughts lead to emotional reactions, which produce physical sensations and responses. Understanding thoughts and emotions as a physical experience may be the most direct, as well as the easiest, way for you to recognize your various states of mind.

In some situations your main thought or emotion may not be that obvious. All that you'll experience is a physical sensation. Body-awareness allows you to catch stress and short-circuit it before it gets really out of control. You can actually use this awareness as a kind of barometer, a window to your emotional and mental status.

I want you to think of a situation that made you feel angry or upset. Focus on the sensations in your body as you think about this upsetting situation. Observe how they feel. What's their quality? Are these sensations squeezing, pulsating, throbbing, hot, sharp, dull, jabbing, or heavy? Where are they located? Do you feel tension in your chest, abdomen, forehead, jaw, or shoulders?

 Set your timer for two minutes and close your eyes. Bring your awareness to the nature of your physical sensations as you think about an upsetting event. Take a few moments to breathe deeply and calm yourself before returning to the book.

Were you able to feel the nature of your body in response to a mental and emotional upset? Could you just be present to what you were experiencing without any need to change the experience?

I would now ask you to observe what *happens* to your thoughts and emotions, in response to an upsetting situation, as you bring your awareness solely to the physical expression of the upset in your body.

 Set your timer for two minutes. Close your eyes and observe what happens to your thoughts and emotional reactions in response to an emotionally upsetting event as you focus on your body.

As you stepped out of the story and focused on the physical feelings of the upset state, did the energy of the mental tension start to dissolve? What you're trying for when you focus on what's going on in your body when you're stressed is to no longer be the "I" who is starring in an upsetting story. Instead, you refocus on the physical experience that's occurring in response to the story. The next time you're mentally or emotionally upset, consciously focus your attention on your body and its sensations instead of the storyline that's talking about how upset you are.

Breathing is also a physical manifestation of your thoughts. You explored in the last chapter how breath control can make your mind and body relax when your mind doesn't seem to want to. You can also use the breath to relax specific parts of the body. Bringing your attention to your body and focusing your breathing into the place of physical tension is a wonderful way to help further release this body stress.

In this next exercise, you will be imagining that you're directly focusing your breathing into the area of physical tension. It's like massaging a tense muscle to help relieve the spasm.

I want you to think of a situation that made you feel angry or upset. Focus on the sensations in your body as you think about this upsetting situation. Then consciously take a deep and calm breath and imagine that you're breathing directly into and out of any areas of tension.

It may sound strange at first. You might be thinking, "How can I breathe into my eyes?" What I mean by this is that I want you to mentally send the breath to that area. Imagine that your breath is coming into and flowing out of the tense body part. With every breath out you'll let go of some tension and promote a natural relaxation response. A relaxed body leads to a relaxed mind.

 Set your timer for two minutes for this exercise. Close your eyes. Think of an upsetting situation and consciously direct your breath to the area of physical tension. Take a few deep breaths to calm down before returning to the text.

What happened to the body tension as you directed your breath, in a calm and deep manner, to that spot? Did you find that it helped that part of your body to relax? Using your breath in this way can really help to release tension.

The following are exercises that you can practice to help develop mindfulness of your physical sensations.

1. For five to ten minutes in the morning and/or evening, sit quietly and simply observe the physical sensations in your body. Label them as you notice them e.g., "Now squeezing," "Twisting," "Throbbing," or "Pulsating discomfort."

2. During the day, whenever you can, try to be aware of the physical sensations that are present in the body.

3. Whenever an upsetting event arises during the day, pause and pay attention to what you're feeling physically.

4. Whenever a happy event arises during the day, pause and pay attention to what you're feeling in your body.

5. Choose an environmental cue that will remind you to be mindful of the physical sensation that you're experiencing at that moment. This could be, for example, before you eat, brush your teeth, wash your face, take a walk, or answer the phone. *Pause* and *pay attention.*

6. Set your wristwatch or cell phone so that an alarm goes off every two to three hours to remind you to be mindful of the physical sensation in that moment.

7. Put *Post-it* notes up around your house, in your car, or at work to remind you to be mindful of the physical sensations in that moment.

8. If you're bringing your awareness to your body as often as you can during the day, you have an opportunity to encourage mental and physical relaxation and decrease your tendency toward stressful reactions.

9. When you're under stress, bring your attention to the place where you're experiencing the physical sensations. Then consciously bring your breath to that place and imagine breathing in and out of that site until you're feeling relaxed.

## Body Scan

The *Body Scan* is another great way to increase your awareness of your body and promote physical relaxation. During the scan, you'll be bringing your attention, in a very systematic way, to the sensations that appear in your body. Let's get right to it and do a Body-Scan exercise right now. This practice can be done lying down or sitting, whatever you prefer. It's probably wise not to do this in bed as you might fall asleep.

It's best to practice with an empty stomach. Remove your glasses if you wear them and take off your shoes. Make sure you're wearing comfortable clothing. Choose a place that's quiet, where you don't have too many distractions.

If you choose to practice lying down, put a pillow under your knees and you'll be more comfortable.

If you sit in a chair to practice, sit toward the edge. Your back doesn't need to touch the chair back. Make sure your feet are flat on the floor and your hands are relaxed in your lap.

In the *Body Scan* you'll deliberately bring your attention to each part of your body one at a time. You'll focus on the physical sensations that you're feeling in each body part before moving on to the next.

Be curious. What does each sensation actually feel like? You're interested in experiencing any sensation in its pure form, as it really is. Don't focus on the story you have about how much a sensation hurts, or how you want to get rid of it, or how unfair it is. You'll also see how those sensations tend to change as you observe them and mindfully breathe.

The breath is a key component of this practice. As you discovered in the previous section, breathing has a tremendous ability to promote mental and physical relaxation. By bringing the breath to any place where you're feeling physical tension, you'll gradually release this tension. The physical release of tension then promotes a state of mental peace.

Breathe into the area that you're focusing on. Stay at each body site for two complete breaths. Breathe in a controlled, even, smooth, deep and quiet manner. Breathe in and out as if the breath is coming from that designated site. A complete cycle of inhalation and exhalation counts as one breath.

 Read through the following instructions. Then try to scan your body just as you've read. You can come back to this exercise and read through the instructions each time you do it, but I think you'll really get the hang of it quite quickly.

- Bring your attention to your *body as a whole.* Be generally aware of any sensations. Is there any discomfort, or pressure anywhere? Do you feel relaxed or tense?
- Imagine, as you breathe in, that you're breathing from your toes all the way to the top of your head. When you breathe out, imagine the process in reverse, breathing from the top of your head to your toes. Do this for two complete breaths.
- Next bring your attention *to the top of your head, forehead and eyes.* As you focus on this area, breathe in for two controlled breaths. Make sure your breathing is smooth, quiet, even, long and deep. Notice whatever you're physically feeling. Is the physical sensation hot, cold, tight, loose, vibrating, calm, or itchy? Notice how your body responds. If you notice tension in an area after two breaths, just continue to breathe deeply into that area until it relaxes.

- Next think about your *face... your mouth... your tongue... your jaw*. Be open to receiving whatever you're experiencing. Don't criticize or judge what you're feeling. It is what it is, neither good nor bad. Can you be with the pure physical sensation without adding a story to it?

- Focus on your *shoulders and neck*. Just breathe. Do the sensations seem to change as you bring your attention to that area?

- Next concentrate on the feeling in your *upper arms... your forearms... your hands*.

- Switch your focus to your *upper chest... your upper back areas*. Feel if there's any tension there. Imagine your breath going into those areas and relaxing them. Breathe out any tension when you exhale. If a thought or emotion arises that distracts you from focusing on your body, that's okay. Recognize the distracting thought, then bring your attention right back to your body and your breath. Let the thought go without attaching to it or dwelling on it. If you seem to be falling asleep and you're doing this exercise lying on the floor, shift to a sitting position, or open your eyes.

- Bring your awareness to your *abdominal area... and your lower back next*. If there's a lot of pain that keeps drawing your attention to any one region, I want you to really focus on that area. Just experience the sensation in that spot for a while. Observe it. See how it changes. Continue to imagine bringing your breath into that spot.

- Bring your attention to *your pelvic region ... your buttocks... your thighs... the back of your legs... your calves, your shins*. Remember; don't judge yourself as a failure if you lose your concentration. It's perfectly normal for this to happen. Simply bring your attention back to your body, to the area of interest.

- Focus on your *ankles, the tops of your feet... the bottoms of your feet*... breathing all the way into your toes.

- Finally, *scan your body* again from your toes to the top of your head. Breathe in completely for one inhalation as you scan. See if there are any areas of tension or discomfort remaining.

Focus your attention on those areas as best you can. Imagine your breath going into those areas and completely relaxing them; then scan from the top of your head to your toes again. Do this finishing scan for two complete breaths.

- To conclude the exercise, I want you to bring yourself out of it gradually and gently. Slowly wiggle your fingers and toes... then your hands and feet. Shrug or roll your shoulders, and finally open your eyes. If you're lying down, roll onto your right side for a moment before sitting up. Slowly push yourself up to a sitting position. Feel your energy returning. Stay still for a few moments before slowly standing.

Your body is alive with sensations. Become familiar with them. The following is a series of formal practice suggestions that will help you develop the technique of the *Body Scan* even further.

1. Practice ten to fifteen minutes of the *Body Scan* in the morning and/or in the evening. If you're practicing for ten to fifteen minutes you can use a timer with an alarm to let you know when your time is up. Another option is to do one, two, three or as many body scans as you want to do in a session depending on the time you want to set aside to do this.

2. Just as you've done with your previous practice exercises, use normal daily activities or times to remind you to bring your awareness to your body. Simply scan your body from your toes to your head, and back down from your head to your toes. Wherever there is a dominant physical sensation stay at that spot and become familiar with it. It's all up to you to think of what times of day, or cues, that you can use to remind yourself to spend a few moments with the sensations in your body. Make a plan and write it down, then stick to it.

3. You can use your *Post-it* notes again as reminders. This time write "body," as a reminder to yourself to do a quick scan of your body when you see the note.

4. Use your phone alarm to remind you to take a *Body Scan* break every two to three hours.

5. Breathe for a minimum of five breath-cycles whenever you bring your awareness to your body during the day.

## Progressive Muscle Relaxation

In this next section you'll be learning the practice of *Progressive Muscle Relaxation.*

Many of us live in a chronic state of muscular tension. It gets worse when we face times of increased stress. You've already learned that whenever you experience anxiety it's expressed in your body. You may not even realize that your muscles are tense all the time. Think about what you do when you're stressed. Do you tense your shoulders, frown, clench your jaw, or hold your breath?

For this exercise, you're going to purposely tense your muscles and then relax them. This will allow you to learn to recognize when your muscles are tense and when they are relaxed. Becoming mindfully aware of the difference between tension and relaxation creates an internal physical alarm, which will let you know when you're starting to feel stressed so that you can do something about it.

For this exercise, please find a quiet place, free of distractions. You may choose to lie down with a pillow under your knees, or sit in a chair. You're going to prepare yourself just as you did in the *Body Scan.* This exercise can be demanding on your body, so if at any time you need to take a break during it, of course, feel free to do so.

As you work through this exercise, you'll squeeze different muscles as hard as you can, making sure not to squeeze them too hard, or so long, that it causes you any harm. You'll tighten the different muscles enough to create discomfort so that you can begin to learn about how your body experiences and expresses stress and pain. Then you will rapidly release the tension all at once. Read through these instructions and when you're done, give *Progressive Muscle Relaxation* a try.

Read through the following instructions. Then try a *Progressive Muscle Relaxation* practice.

- Initially do a quick *Body Scan*. Take two deep breaths. Make sure your breathing is slow, smooth, even, quiet and long. Breathe in from your toes to the top of your head and exhale from your head down through to your toes. This is one complete breath. First, you'll feel the resting sensations in your body as you complete these first two breath-cycles. You'll initially focus on becoming aware of what's going on in your body.

- Start with your forehead. *Lift your eyebrows* as high as they can go. Lift them to the top of your head! Focus on the feeling in the muscle with this intense contraction. If there's a lot of pain, then just ease off a bit. Breathe in slowly, deeply and quietly. Hold the squeeze for as long as it takes to slowly breathe in. Don't hold your breath. When you're ready to breathe out, quickly release the tensed muscle. Just let it go. Allow the muscle to completely relax as you exhale slowly and deeply. Notice how different that muscle feels when it's tense compared to when it's relaxed. Continue to breathe for two more breath-cycles. One complete inhalation and exhalation is a breath-cycle. In and out, breathe into the relaxed muscle, just as you learned in the *Body Scan*. Feel how relaxed that area is afterward. Can you feel the difference?

- Move to your eyes. *Squeeze your eyes tightly shut.* Hold the squeeze for a breath-cycle and then relax. Breathe deeply for two more breath-cycles and feel the relaxed sensation in your eyes.

- Move on to your mouth. *Open your mouth* as wide as you can. Hold your jaw as wide open as you can. Squeeze as long as you breathe in and then let go quickly as you breathe out. Don't force your breath out, just let it release naturally and smoothly. Focus on the relaxation in your jaw for two more breaths. As with the *Body Scan*, you're progressively working down the body.

- Next *lift your shoulders* to your ears. Tense them and then relax. Imagine your breath going into your shoulders and releasing any remaining tension. Notice how your shoulders feel when they're tight compared to when you let go of that tension. Focus on the relaxation in your shoulders for two more breaths.

- Bring both of *your arms up to your shoulders and clench your fists*. Tighten both your arms as much as you can. Feel that tension. Only tense your arms and fists. Don't clench your jaw or raise your shoulders. Breathe in and tighten and then drop your arms. Breathe deeply into both your arms for two breath-cycles. When doing these exercises try not to tense any other parts of your body except for the specific muscle group you're working with. Just imagine your breath going into your arm muscles and back out. Relax them even more as you breathe out. Breathe in and focus on your arms and breathe out and relax.

- Next make a tight *fist with both of your hands* at the same time. Tighten them. Tighter. Tighter... and breathe out and release the fists. Focus on how your hands feel afterward. Breathe in and out for two more breaths.

- Take a deep breath and *expand your chest* as wide as it will go. Notice the feeling of tightness in your chest. Then quickly release the tension in the chest as you breathe out. Breathe deeply, gently and smoothly letting your stomach expand as you breathe in. Focus on the sensation in your chest as you breathe for two more breaths.

- Bring your attention to your abdomen and *squeeze your belly button* so that it tries to touch your spine. Keep squeezing for as long as you can as you take a slow, deep inhalation. At the end of the inhalation let all the tension go quickly and then continue to breathe into your abdomen for two more slow deep breaths.

- *Tighten the muscles in your buttocks*. Hold that tension as you breathe in and let go of the tension all at once as you breathe out. Just rest and breathe feeling the sensation of relaxation in those muscles. Breathe for two more complete breaths as you bring your attention to your buttocks.
- *Flex both of your feet* by stretching your feet upward toward your shins. You're just tensing up your feet and your leg muscles here. Feel the tension in your thighs and lower legs. Hold the tension. Tense up both your legs. Notice how that tension feels and then let it all go. Breathe for two more complete breaths as you feel the physical sensation of release in your feet and thighs.
- Finally, *curl your toes*. Really tighten them up as you breathe in. Curl those toes tightly and release them as you breathe out. Bring your attention to the feeling in your toes for two more complete breaths.
- Finish with a quick *Body Scan*. Breathe in and out for two breaths as you scan for any areas remaining in the body that are still tense. Breathe into those areas, relaxing them with your exhalation.
- At the end of the exercise, when you're ready, open your eyes. Start to move your body, slowly at first. Again, if you're doing this exercise on the floor, roll onto your right side first; push yourself up to a sitting position with your arms. Stand up very slowly.

## Progressive Muscle Relaxation: Short Version

In situations where there's not enough time to go through an entire Progressive Muscle Relaxation exercise, you can practice a shortened version. This means you'll contract and then relax only your larger muscle groups.

Start by tensing and relaxing in sequence:

- *Facial Muscles*
- *Hands*, *Arms*, *Shoulders*, *Neck* all at the same time
- *Stomach*, *Chest* all at the same time
- *Buttocks*, *Feet*, *Legs* all at the same time

Don't forget about your breath. The key is to inhale while you tense the muscle areas, and exhale to release the tension. Remember to take two more complete breaths afterward, feeling the physical sensation of relaxation in the designated muscle group.

The following is an exercise that will help further develop the practice of Progressive Muscle Relaxation.

1. Practice Progressive Muscle Relaxation for ten to fifteen minutes in the morning and/or evening, whatever works for you. Alternatively, do a Progressive Muscle Relaxation practice once, twice or as many times as you want to in a given session.

2. If you're able to, take a break at your desk, or during television commercials, or when you're at your computer and progressively tense and relax your muscles. Gradually your body will learn the difference between these two states and it will become easier and easier to find and release tension. Less tension automatically means less stress.

## How to Deal With Physical Pain

The real test of body-awareness comes when you have to deal with physical pain. This can be from a direct physical injury or a mentally stressful event. As you know, your mental stress is expressed physically.

When there is pain in the body bring your attention to the area of muscular tension.

You have previously learned how slow, deep, smooth, belly breathing, with a prolonged exhalation, lessens stress. If you can direct the breath, like a laser, into the area of pain, this will allow that area to relax and feedback to create additional mental relaxation. This will lessen your pain. Continue to breathe into the area for as long as there is pain. The breath is a wonderful tool for dealing with discomfort.

When you encounter pain you often create a story about it. Remember when my patient Mika was having abdominal cramps and she believed that she had cancer? You might have a headache and worry that it's a brain tumor. If you're having chest pain, it's hard to believe it could be anything but a heart attack even when you've been given the all clear and you know your heart is fine. You probably experience more pain from the anxiety around the story you tell yourself than from the original physical pain.

Bringing awareness to the story can help to lessen the secondary mental pain that accompanies the actual physical discomfort. As you'll learn in the next section, identifying the process of original sensation to subsequent story can help take you out of the storyline and lessen the stressful drama that you create in your mind.

It can be helpful in these situations to take a reality check. As you bring awareness to the story your mind is telling, step back and inquire about the truth of what your mind is saying. For example you may say to yourself, "Do I really have colon cancer? How do I know this? Maybe I need to see my doctor about this. Until then I just don't know what's happening. However it doesn't mean that it's bad."

When you experience a physical discomfort you often put a label on it such as "this horrible pain!" It can be helpful to step out of the concept of pain and bring mindfulness to the situation. Try to experience the "pain" as the changing physical sensation that it really is. Observe it and create some distance between you and it. What does it really feel like? Is it a stinging, sharp, vibrating, hot, or heavy sensation? As you bring your continual attention to the area, the sensation of pain will start to change, perhaps lessen and ultimately your mind will be drawn elsewhere.

## Practice

1. Initially, a formal practice of the *Body Scan* and *Progressive Muscle Relaxation*, where you set aside a daily designated time to practice body-awareness, will help you to train yourself to become aware of muscle tension as it reflects your mental state. Regular practice of body-awareness through these exercises will also lead to physical and mental relaxation.

2. Support your practice on a daily basis by using environmental cues, *Post-it* notes, and a phone or watch alarm, as you did in the breath-awareness exercises, to remind you to become aware of what tension is present in the body at designated times.

3. Do quick versions of the body-awareness exercises when you don't have time for a longer session. Every bit helps. Do the *Body Scan* and *Progressive Muscle Relaxation* before and after events that you know will be stressful.

## Summary

- When you're emotionally upset, this is reflected in your body. If you relax your body, your mind relaxes and vice versa.
- Thoughts lead to emotional reactions, which in turn produce physical sensations and responses. Understanding thoughts and emotions as a physical experience may be the most direct and easiest way for you to recognize your various states of mind.
- You can use your breathing to specifically relax parts of the body by bringing your attention to an area of tension and focusing your breathing into that area.

- The next time you're mentally or emotionally upset, consciously focus your attention on your body and its sensations, instead of the storyline in your mind that's dwelling on how upset you are.
- The *Body Scan* and *Progressive Muscle Relaxation* are two important techniques that will improve your body-awareness.
- The *Body Scan* makes you aware of the sensations in your body.
- *Progressive Muscle Relaxation* teaches you to identify the difference between a muscle that's contracted and one that's at rest.
- When in pain, direct your breathing into the area that's bothering you. This will allow that area to relax, which will have a calming effect and lessen your discomfort.
- Try not to create a story about your pain. Recognize that your worries about the pain are likely unfounded. Mindfully try to experience the pain as simply a changing physical sensation instead of labeling it as a "horrible pain."
- Mental stress is expressed in the body. A relaxed body leads to a calmer mind.

# 9
## *Mindfulness of the Process of Thought Development*

**Y**OU'VE PROBABLY HAD THE EXPERIENCE of seeing a man, whom you've never met, and you've instantly had a story about him pop into your mind. He may be too fat, thin, selfish, mean or even happy. You've also had the experience of seeing food, a type of car, clothing, art, or jewelry and suddenly your inner voice is telling a story about how much you want the item or don't want it.

Your inner voice will pop up commenting, criticizing, or comparing, when you talk to another person, forget to go to the bank, go off your diet, buy something, look in the mirror, or do pretty much anything. That inner voice is often harsh and may say that you yourself are mean, stupid, ugly, not worthy, unlovable or wrong. It comments on everything.

As you have previously discovered, you are never just dealing with an original event as it is, you only see it through the lens of your experience and belief system. It's very helpful to examine the *process* of how you got from the initial event (seeing a person, eating food, talking to someone) to the inner voice and the story that popped up around this event.

By asking your mind to explore and identify this process, you distance yourself from the story's content and your emotional identification with it. Your mind becomes more interested in the task of finding and following the sequence of events from original perception to subsequent story. When you  examine the process itself, you're examining something that now will seem to be taking place outside of you, instead of something that is a representation of you personally.

You can learn to "externalize," or examine something, as someone looking at it from a distance. Not only will you benefit from a more thorough understanding of your own reactions, you will be able to then act from a position of non-identification. You're free to become mindfully aware of what happened and how it happened and then you're free to choose how you would like to respond.

## What's the sensation and what's the story?

I find that just bringing mindfulness to the mental state alone, may not be effective enough to make me really let go of the story. I may be able to identify the emotion or thought (e.g., fear, anger, sadness) but it's still *my* fear, *my* anger, or *my* sadness. It can be hard sometimes, when a story is making me very emotional, to not personally identify with my own tall-tale as having more than a little truth. This is where identifying the process from sensation to story can be really helpful.

I was out shopping the other day and I found a phone that was really expensive. I bought it and shortly after that my mind started to say, "How could I have bought that phone? It was way too expensive. I didn't need one that fancy. I made a bad choice. That was the wrong thing to do!" My mind was telling me that I had done something wrong and I believed it. I was feeling anxious.

Where did this story come from? My parents were immigrants and had to work hard when they came to this country. The message I learned when I was young was that it was important to save money and not spend it. It made no difference that I was an adult and a doctor and could certainly afford the phone. To my mind, I had not followed the part of my belief system that deals with saving and I had made a big mistake.

However, my mistake was not purchasing the phone. My mistake was getting caught up in my own story about the purchase, a story that was filled with guilt and stress. The stress was created because I believed the story my mind was telling me about what I had done. I gave my mind the task of trying to identify the original sensation and the subsequent story with its associated emotional and physical reaction. This allowed me to step out of the storyline and the subsequent drama created from the ownership of the story. I could then choose whether I wanted to keep the phone, or return it, based on a more realistic assessment of the purchase.

Your mind is very quick, so you often just hear your mind's story without ever identifying the original event that started the whole thing. You can train your mind to look for the initial sensation and the subsequent story. Mindfulness is a technique that allows you to observe how your mind works in order to help relieve stress.

Unless you are aware of what's happening all you might hear from your mind is that you are hopeless and bad. At this point you need to look at the process of how your mind is functioning. Ask, "*What's the sensation and what's the story?*" My response, in this instance, might be:

- *The sensation was I bought a phone.*
- *The story is that I made a mistake and I am bad.*

In reviewing this chain of events, from initial sensation or perception, to a massive and emotional concept or story, it will become apparent that your stories may have no true sense of connection, or relevance to what you initially experienced.

Another example might be when you're watching TV and you don't get out for a walk or run. Your inner voice may say, "Look what you just did. You sat around watching TV. Don't you know that you're supposed to be exercising? You're so hopeless. You'll never lose weight. You're fat, lazy and hopeless."

By asking yourself, "What was the sensation and what was the story?" you'll quickly see the grand leap of judgment from just choosing to watch TV to being a horrible, hopeless individual. Identifying sensation and story allows you to see how your mind can make up stories that are unbelievable and grossly over-exaggerated. Discover your initial perception or sensation and follow the process by which a story emerges. You'll be better able to really understand that when a story appears, it doesn't mean that it comes from a place of wisdom, that it's helpful, or that it's even necessarily true.

The initial internal or external sensation may not even be that significant all by itself, but your mind creates its stories around the event. These stories are based on how the event compares to your internalized belief system. You unconsciously are asking yourself, "Is what I see, hear, feel, touch, smell or think considered to be in agreement with what I believe already? Do I feel safe? "

The initial experience rapidly becomes, not about the person, sensation, object or thought that started the whole cascade, but rather about the story you have created in response. These stories may not accurately reflect what's really happening at the moment. Remember, that your internal belief system was a learned response and its purpose was originally to maintain your parents' love and acceptance. You make rapid judgments about present events by gauging to what degree new events agree, or fit in, with your past beliefs.

Identify what actually happened; that you bought a phone, or watched TV instead of going for a run. Recognize that you then created a story about it. Finally, refocus on the original event more mindfully and with greater openness and acceptance.

The idea is to let go of your creation, your story. When you let go of the story, you can finally see that the only truth of the situation rests in the original sensation or perception. Apply this concept to stressful events and watch your stories crumble into the imaginary dust that is their true nature. It's going to take practice, but every time you succeed in de-stressing, even a little bit, it's a huge victory for both your body and your peace of mind.

Another thing that often happens is that your mind has a characteristic way of reacting to a situation that is specific to you personally. You may only become aware of your characteristic reaction when it reaches the point of causing your inner voice to make a final remark or criticism. All you may be aware of is this final remark, this judgmental statement. You may not be conscious of the underlying process that began with an initial sensation and continued through the subsequent story, only to finally arrive at this judgmental statement.

Some of the common judgmental statements are:

- *I am so bad*
- *This is terrible*
- *I can't believe I did that*
- *I am always making a fool of myself*
- *This is horrible*
- *I am in real trouble*
- *I hate myself*
- *I am so stupid*
- *I am hopeless*

Your personal characteristic reaction is like a habit. It's a process by which you arrive at a judgmental statement that you then hear in your mind. All that you are likely aware of is this negative, judgmental statement and its associated feeling. Many times, you might not even remember what triggered your reaction. The initiating event could have been an internal thought triggered by a memory, or it could have been an external sensation and your reaction to it. However, when you consciously try to figure out what might have been the initial sensation and what story you told yourself about it, your mind then has a task to do. This task creates some space between the real you and the self-critical, demeaning comments that your mind makes during its characteristic reactions. You will begin to see that there is this repetitive pattern to how your mind works. With practice you can start to see this sequence in action as it unfolds.

Your personal, characteristic reaction-sequence does not necessarily result in a judgmental statement. Your personal pattern of reaction might be expressed in a nonverbal way. You may just feel depressed, sad or scared. You may feel a physical sense of what you are experiencing. When you become aware of negative emotions, or atypical physical symptoms, tracking backwards in search of an underlying story or process can be very helpful.

Somewhat less common than the self-critical, judgmental mind is its cousin the comparing mind. When your mind is comparing, it tells you that you are better than whatever it is that you are comparing yourself to. For example your mind might say:

- *Look at those terrible jeans he is wearing.*
- *She is driving a beat up Ford.*
- *He is really fat.*
- *She is so messy when she eats.*
- *He only makes ____ dollars.*

With this type of comment, your inner child is comparing itself to something in the external environment, or to a thought or image that has arisen internally. Even though you might not be consciously aware of the full, internal conversation, there is a series of additional unspoken comments that accompany such a comparison. What has not been said, but is intuitively known, is the full comparative statement.

To understand the full comparative statement you would examine the fact to story process. You'd fill in the gaps between what the original fact was, such as watching someone eat, and then examine what that meant to you. What becomes evident is that the very statements that make you feel superior also make you feel safe and worthy.

Let's look at the previous group of comparative comments. This time, we'll fill in the unspoken statements that accompany a comparative comment, in other words, what is known but not being said.

- *Look at those terrible jeans he is wearing.*
- *I own a designer pair of jeans. I dress better than he does. I am way more elegant.*

- *She is driving a beat up Ford.*
- *I drive an Acura. I have a better car. I am more successful.*

- *He is so fat.*
- *I am thinner. I am healthier and look better.*

- *She is so messy when she eats.*
- *I am more careful when I eat. I am not a slob.*

- *He only makes ____ dollars.*
- *I make more money than that. I am wealthier than he is.*

When you catch yourself making a comparative comment, don't let it race through your mind unexamined. Stop the comment in its tracks and be mindful of what triggered the comment and the unspoken, implied thoughts that are really a part of the full statement. Consider the initial trigger. Look for the story. Be mindful of the process by which the comparative comment came to be voiced.

Normally, when you practice mindfulness you are being mindful of a mental, emotional or physical state. In practicing mindfulness of a process, you are bringing your awareness to how the state is being created. It's easier to be less invested in, or attached to, a process, the process of sensation to story. Let go of the story and the stress that comes with judging, comparing and criticizing will also be released.

## Clinging To or Letting Go of the Story

You have a truly amazing mind. You're capable of inventing and getting caught up in your own story but you can also witness the story from the perspective of your observing mind. Normally you unconsciously identify and take ownership of the inciting sensation, or deny it and push it away. However, the other conscious option is to practice mindfulness and allow it to pass by as just another thought.

*You can use this aspect of "clinging to," or "letting go of," your stories as an object of your mindful awareness.* The act of clinging, or letting go, becomes another part of the process of how your mind works. Bring your attention and analysis to this process and it will become another interesting task for your mind to follow. This will also provide you with a sense of distance from an emotional episode. When your mind has a job to do, the focus is on the task and not the content of the story.

Imagine you have just eaten a piece of pizza and it wasn't on your diet. Your mind is saying that you are bad and useless. At that point, you have a choice. You can believe and take ownership of the self-judgment, or you can allow the judgement to pass by without identifying with it.

When an emotion arises, bring mindfulness to how you're responding. Ask yourself, *"What's my relationship to the story?"* Are you clinging or letting go? Fully experience how you're relating to the story mentally and physically. Are you becoming the story, owning the pain, fear, anger etc.? Or are you able to just observe the mental state without identifying with it? Can it simply pass by like the wind?

Is there an urgency, resignation, or heaviness to your thoughts? Is there a squeezing, or gripping feeling in your belly? Are you sweating? Is your heartbeat rapid, or your shoulders tense? Bring mindfulness to another layer of your complex, thinking mind.

## Making a Choice: *What needs to be done now?*

Mindfulness is not just about bringing awareness to what you're experiencing and how your mind works. It provides you with an opportunity to make a more conscious and wise choice about how to respond to what your mind is presenting. This pivotal choice-point comes at the interface of the awareness between what's happening and your response. Observe how your mind works as it creates stories that are based on a childhood belief system and then distorts reality. Now you can start to make adult rather than child-based choices. You have the ability at that critical juncture to either go blindly along with whatever your mind says, or to choose a healthier path.

Here's another example. Your mind has just started to say, "How could you have said that? That was horrible. What a mistake you made. You'll never live that down!" Typically, you might have reacted with a sense of ownership of these statements and continued the negative train of thought. Naturally, this would have increased your anxiety and fear. However, by using mindfulness, at the point of awareness, you could now ask, *"What needs to be done now?"* You're calling on a wiser, more balanced, part of your consciousness, which may give you the answer. Often the answer is to do nothing and just let the current mind-state pass.

The significance in calling on this part of your consciousness is that you are choosing to step out of the constant self-referencing of all experience, the self-referencing that leads to your stress and pain. This "stepping out", will allow you to be with what is, for what it is, rather than having to endure whatever stress and drama you create from it. You really do have a choice.

## What remains after the clinging goes?

The last aspect of the process of thought development involves bringing mindfulness to what remains when the clinging goes. As you've already discovered, no thought or emotion stays forever. It will ultimately pass on. At that moment when the identification has passed and before the next sensation arises what do you experience? Ask yourself, "*What remains after the clinging goes?*"

There is a sense of stillness that exists in between the various thoughts that you have. It's a wonderful place to rest and experience the world. Bring mindfulness to this moment and experience physically in your body what stillness feels like. You can use this physical memory as an anchor to gauge whether you're clinging to, or letting go of, what you're experiencing.

What you're really doing with mindfulness and the other suggestions that you've read so far, is discovering how your own mind functions. You have an initial provoking perception, or sensation, but then your mind takes over. The thoughts that arise appear spontaneously. It's like playing an old pinball game where your thoughts are the ball. You eject the ball into play and then it follows its own course, banking off one pillar and then the next, until it finally exits. The initial sensation is received by your mind and then it's shaped by previous memories and beliefs, until a story is created that exits into your consciousness.

*Thinking is simply a conditioned, automatic process, operating independently of conscious control. It's a mental function. You're not your thoughts!*

Bringing mindfulness to the process of thinking is a wonderful way to get your mind to follow what's actually happening. It gives you some much-needed distance and stops you from identifying with what's happening.

## Mindfulness of the Flow of the Energy of Thoughts

When you brought mindfulness to the breath, as you recall, you just followed the breath and its qualities. You can bring this same mindfulness to the flow of the energy of your thoughts. When a chain of thought arises, step out of the content and just observe and feel the energy of the thoughts, how the intensity changes, how it quickly rises and then fades away and how long it lasts. You are not interested in the content. You are feeling the energy of the mind.

Remember the technique of labeling your thoughts and feelings? As you become more experienced in mindfulness, the ability to engage your experience mindfully, without using labeling, will allow you to be present to what is being experienced in its pure form. When you introduce a label such as happy, sad, angry, fearful etc. there is an associated, personal, conditioned value that goes with the label which can influence your connection to what is being experienced.

Mindfulness, without labeling, allows a greater awareness of the ebb and flow of the energy and intensity of your thoughts in their pure form. Once again, this awareness will help you to get some much-needed distance from the thoughts that are the source of your stress.

## Practice

1. Over the course of the next week be especially mindful of your emotions.
2. When an emotional episode occurs, see if you can recognize the initial thought or sensation, as opposed to the story and thoughts that came after.
3. See if you can recognize some pivotal choice points between your awareness of what's happening and your response.
4. When a negative train of thought arises, ask yourself, "*What needs to be done now?*"

## Summary

- Your inner voice is always commenting, criticizing, or comparing and is often harsh and judgmental.
- It's helpful to examine the *process* of how you got from the initial event (seeing a person, eating food, talking to someone) to the inner voice and the story that popped up around this event.
- By asking yourself, "*What was the sensation and what was the story?*," you're free to become mindfully aware of what happened, how it happened and then to choose how best to react.
- By mindfully observing, "*What's my relationship to the story?*" you can determine if you'd prefer to cling to, or let go of, related negative thoughts and emotions.
- There's a pivotal choice point, at the interface of the awareness between what's happening and your response, where you can ask yourself, "*What needs to be done now?*"
- There's a sense of stillness that exists between the thoughts that you have and you will discover this stillness when you stop clinging to the stories that the inner voice is telling you.

# 10

# Mindfulness: Integrative Practice

NOW IT'S TIME TO PUT TOGETHER all the principles of mindfulness that you've learned so far, into a concise, clear, integrated practice. Here are the **ABC**'s of mindfulness:

## A is for Awareness

The first principle of mindfulness is *awareness* of what's happening.

Whenever you can remember to do so, ask yourself, *"What's happening?"* The hardest part of mindfulness is remembering to be mindful. Your mind starts telling stories and it's so easy to get carried away, but you need to step back and observe. You do this mental 'stepping back' by asking yourself questions. Your mind loves to do tasks. Ask yourself, *"What's happening?"* and it will bring you instantly back into the present moment and out of the trance-like nature of your stories.

It's important to remember that what you're asking is, *"What's happening?"* and not, *"What am I experiencing?"* Posing the question in this fashion takes the "I" out of the experience. You're just observing an event that's happening. You're asking your mind to think about what's going on from the perspective of an observer rather than as the principal actor.

In response to this question, you can *re-label* the experience objectively. Your response might be *"Now anger, now sadness, now pain,"* instead of, *"I'm angry. I'm sad. I'm hurt."* The "I" is not part of the experience. As soon as you personalize what's happening, your stories will quickly multiply along with your negative thoughts. You'll get caught up in the perceived drama of the moment.

Some mental events do not have a lot of energy behind them and just bringing your awareness to them is enough to allow them to simply fade away. However, there will be lots of experiences that are quite emotionally charged and more effort will be necessary to deal with them.

## B is for Body and Breath

The second principle of mindfulness is to anchor your experience in your *body*.

Ask your mind the question, *"What's being felt?"* Bring your attention to what's happening in your *body*. How are your mental and emotional states being reflected as physical sensations? In grounding your attention in the physical sensations, you're stepping out of the storyline. The experience itself will become less personal and less threatening. You won't be focusing on statements that include the word "I", so there won't be an "I" that is upset anymore. Instead, perhaps there will just be a twisting, squeezing and/or hot sensation that's being experienced.

*Breathing* is also part of your body-awareness. When you notice that you're tense, ask yourself, *"What's happening to my breathing at this moment?"* Notice if it has become shallow or uneven, or if you have been holding your breath.

Bring mindfulness to your breath and just *follow* it without trying to change it. Mindfulness of the breath will lead to it becoming more relaxed. A calm breath leads to a calm mind.

If you're extremely stressed, *consciously control* your breathing. Start to breathe in a slow, deep, quiet, smooth fashion, from your abdomen and with a prolonged exhalation. Connect the breath and the body to help to calm yourself down.

When you're experiencing a strong physical sensation, such as pain or tension, consciously bring the relaxed breath to the site in the body where the physical tension is being felt. Breathe into and out of that specific spot. Imagine that you're directing the breath into the area of physical discomfort. This calming attention will relax the knot of stress and lessen the pain in the area.

The breath supports every moment of mindfulness. It's of utmost importance!

## C is for Connection

If a particular thought or emotion is very powerful, bring your awareness to the process of how the mind functions. Stepping out of the content helps to lessen the identification.

Ask yourself, *"What's the fact and what's the story?"* Identify the original thought and this will allow you to witness how your mind creates wild stories about everything.

Ask, *"What's my relationship to the story?"* Are you clinging to, or letting go of, the story?

Ask, *"What needs to be done?"* You have the ability to make a wise choice and to stop yourself from owning the automatic, conditioned response.

Ask, *"What remains after the clinging goes?"* Can you rest in the stillness between your thoughts?

Ask, *"What does the flow of mind-energy feel like?"* Can you rest in the energy of thought movement and not its content?

## Practice

Mindfulness is really a process that you will be constantly learning. Don't be impatient if you continue to be caught by your thoughts and your emotional states of mind. You have had many years of practice at your old way of thinking. It will require lots of practice to relearn a whole new way of looking at, and dealing with, your own mind. The important thing is that you try to practice mindfulness every day. Practice as often as you can.

Initially, it will be easier to let the thoughts and stories, that are not so emotionally charged, pass by. However, the ones that are more important to you will continue to catch you and make you ride their train. It may be helpful to come back to those events when you're away from the experiences that triggered the emotions. Replay them in your mind, in private, later, with mindfulness. Slowly, you will learn how to bring mindfulness to these emotionally charged events as well. You will have plenty of opportunity to practice with these more charged episodes, stories and thoughts, as they have a tendency to continue to replay themselves.

When you practice mindfulness on a continual basis, all of your sensations start to be treated equally. When you're mindful of your physical sensations consistently, then you'll start to treat a thought or emotion as just another sensation that comes and goes. Your thoughts will ultimately have less power over you. Therefore, there may be value in practicing the labeling of all sensations as they arise. Label your sensations as often as you can for now, although the eventual goal is for this labeling to be unnecessary.

It takes courage to be willing to face thoughts, emotions and physical sensations with acceptance and without judgment. It's not easy to just be with what arises but you'll get better at it. You don't have to change or deny anything. The key is not to identify with a thought, but to simply see it as another bit of mental energy that traps, confuses and entices you into believing that it's real and it's you. It's not! It's just your conditioned history speaking to you. Your true self is much greater and wiser!

Mindfulness doesn't free you from having thoughts; it allows you to be free to have those thoughts. In other words, it's a wonderful technique that liberates you from your conditioned, automatic, reflexive mind. It allows you to approach your life from a place of greater insight, wisdom and compassion.

There are several things you can do everyday to start practicing mindfulness:

1. For five to ten minutes in the morning and/or in the evening, sit quietly and simply observe your thoughts, emotions and

physical sensations. Label them as you notice them e.g., "thinking," "feeling," or "a physical sensation." You can also be more specific and label the sensations as "judging," "sadness," or "a squeezing sensation."

2. When a negative or unpleasant event occurs, stop and observe the thoughts, emotions and physical sensations that arise as a consequence of the event. *Stop and pay attention.*

3. When a happy or pleasant event occurs, stop and observe the thoughts, emotions and physical sensations that arise as a consequence of this type of event as well.

4. During the day, whenever you can, try to *label* whatever internal or external sensation comes into your consciousness.

5. Choose an environmental cue that will help you to be mindful. This could be: before you sit down for breakfast, brush your teeth, read the paper, go to the store, or when a certain ad comes on TV.

6. Set your wristwatch or cell phone so that an alarm goes off every few hours. Whenever the alarm goes off, stop and try to be mindful of what you're thinking, feeling and physically experiencing at that moment.

7. Put *Post-it* notes up around the house, in your car or at your place of work to remind you to be mindful.

8. Remember the **ABC**'s of Mindfulness (Awareness, Body, Breath and Connection). Ask yourself: *"What's happening?" "What's being felt?" "What's happening to my breathing at this moment?"* and *"What's my connection?"*

## Summary

- You constantly identify with your thoughts and emotions.
- Mindfulness is an accepting, non-judging, non-attached and compassionate awareness of your experience as it unfolds in the present moment.
- Mindfulness is the cultivated ability to be present to what you experience without having to react to it or change it.

- Mindfulness encourages you to be intentionally aware of your thoughts, emotions and physical sensations whenever possible.
- Mindfulness asks you to label your thoughts, to not judge them, to just accept them as mental energy that arises and then as quickly moves on.
- Be an observer in your own mind and body and try not to identify so strongly with your thoughts and emotions.
- Practicing more compassion for yourself is an important aspect of mindfulness.
- Mindfully focus on what occurs in your body during emotional responses, and you can learn how to calm yourself sooner.
- Thoughts, emotions and physical sensations don't last forever and will change or go away. Just be patient.

# 11

# Meditation: Sitting in Stillness

WHEN YOU HEAR THE WORD MEDITATION what does it mean to you? Do you have images of it being a weird cult-like practice where you stop thinking for yourself and see visions? Or where you rest in some strange celestial space? Meditation has been around for thousands of years and has been practiced, in some form, by all religions and cultures. It's actually quite mainstream.

When I first started to meditate, I wasn't quite sure what I was getting into. I had heard about this technique that was supposed to help with stress. Initially, it was difficult to maintain my concentration on one object. My mind would wander all over the place. At certain times, I was more committed than at others.

My body would ache from sitting. However, I deeply sensed that this was a valuable technique and if I could just continue to commit myself to meditating, I would see some benefit. Slowly, I began to be able to sit and concentrate for longer periods. I also began to notice some changes in myself. On the days that I would meditate, I was more likely to be at peace, less reactive to life's events and more accepting of others and myself.

Unfortunately, when life became very busy and hectic, I often decided that I didn't have the time to meditate and I felt even more stressed. As time went on, I would notice that after I meditated I would go to work and suddenly it seemed as if my mind had shifted into a lower gear. I was really present to what was going on. I felt happier, my inner voice was quiet, and I could listen to people without judgment and with a sense of connection and understanding.

The effects of meditation don't just happen while you're meditating. They can last throughout the day.

I have made a commitment to meditate on a regular basis because I have experienced positive changes in myself. This didn't happen suddenly. There were no lights, or explosions of discovery. It was a slow process requiring commitment and perseverance. My meditations are not all "great." However, I have experienced changes in myself that truly have been beneficial and have allowed me to live my life in a more peaceful and happier fashion.

In the practice of meditation, the mind slowly becomes focused and quiet as you enter into a state of stillness and silence, moving beyond your thinking mind. In that open expansive state, you may feel a certain connection to your true inner wisdom and to all living beings.

Some people say, "My mind is too busy. I could never sit in stillness!" My reply to that is, "Do you have something that you're passionate about?" When you're dancing, playing sports, listening to music, taking pictures, or painting are you totally fixated on what you're doing? Does time stand still? Does anything else exist at that moment? We all have the ability to deeply concentrate and these experiences in our everyday lives are a form of meditation. Sitting in meditation is just a matter of training the mind to become focused on a specific, chosen object of attention.

Meditation has been demonstrated to have positive physical and mental effects. It decreases anxiety, improves depression, and reduces the frequency and intensity of panic attacks. People with cancer tend to cope better. It improves high blood pressure and helps with various painful disorders.

Recent scientific investigations have demonstrated that there are functional and structural changes that occur in the brain when a person meditates. A brain scan, called an MRI, has revealed that in meditation, parts of the brain that are responsible for positive emotional states become more active. Another brain scan, called a CT scan, has revealed a change in the size of part of the brain, called the cortex, with meditation. I find this information very exciting and motivating. Through meditation, we have the ability to change the way our brains work. We are not trapped forever in brains that can't change. We can move beyond the idea of, "That's who I am and I can't change!"

As you meditate, unconscious negative thoughts and emotions from your past may arise. Meditation allows you to discover these thoughts and emotions, to examine them and with awareness, acceptance and self-compassion, allow them to dissolve.

Meditation also provides a way to proceed along a spiritual path. When you're resting in that calm, centered space of awareness and openness, you may feel a sense of universal connection to all of existence. You move beyond the narrow focus of an "I"-based perspective.

## Twelve Principle Points of Practice

Before you sit down to begin your first meditation practice, you'll be glad to know that you've already started! Just by doing the previous breathing and mindfulness exercises you've been doing a form of meditation. The object of your focus, your breathing for example, is always slipping away as the mind naturally wanders and jumps around. It helps to know a few more things about what to expect and how to go about your practice in order to really enjoy its benefits. These twelve principle practice points will help you get started and stay committed, so that you can really begin to take advantage of all that meditation has to offer.

### Purpose

Why are you meditating? Is it to achieve calmness and peace of mind, or are you also trying to find a greater truth of existence beyond yourself? Bring awareness to your purpose without striving to achieve it. You can set your intention for meditation at the beginning of each sitting.

## Place

Choose a space that you can dedicate to meditation. It can be anywhere in your house, but it should be a place where you'll have some peace and quiet with few interruptions. If you meditate in the same place all the time, you will naturally come to associate that location with meditation and you'll begin to relax just by being there.

## Time of Day

Everyone has his or her own daily rhythm. Some people like to meditate in the morning when they first get up, as their minds are naturally quieter. Others prefer afternoons, or when they go to bed to help them sleep better. Choose a time that suits you, but try to be consistent. Make a daily appointment with yourself for that time period. It's best not to meditate right before, or after eating, as the process of digestion will interfere with your concentration, as will feelings of intense hunger. Choose what works best for you personally and then stick with it!

## Focus Your Attention

When meditating, you'll need to pick a focus for your attention. You might choose to focus on your breathing, a light, a sound, a mantra, or whatever the most prominent, mental, or physical sensation happens to be at that time. A mantra is a combination of syllables or words. For some, awareness itself is the object of their attention. When you have chosen a focus for your meditation, it's important to stick to that one object of focus at first, in order to create some consistency in your practice.

## Duration of Practice

In the beginning, you should start with shorter meditation times and then gradually build up to longer intervals. Initially, try for five to ten minutes, once a day. As you continue to progress, you can increase your time by five to ten minutes weekly or whatever seems right for you. With practice, over time, you'll be able to meditate for anywhere up to an hour or longer per day. Don't panic! Life can get hectic but any time that you can commit to meditation is time well spent. Use your watch or cell phone alarm, or even an egg timer, to signal the end of the designated meditation period. That way, you don't have to worry about the time and it helps to develop the persistence to practice until your designated time is up.

## Predictability

In order to see some benefit from meditation, it's important to meditate on a daily basis. Make it a habit. It's only with continued practice that you will develop stability and peace of mind. If you truly can't take the time to meditate daily then make an attempt to meditate as often as you can. If you miss a day, don't worry; just form the intention in your mind to make this a part of your daily routine.

## Making it a Priority

We all lead very busy lives and in order to find time to practice you may have to be creative with the time you have. You may have to decrease the amount of time you spend watching TV, on the computer, or reading, in order to give yourself the time you'll need to meditate. Let your family and friends know not to interrupt you and that this time is your quiet time. Make it a priority. Your health is important. Take a few minutes to meditate on especially hectic days, wherever and whenever you can, but don't forget that it takes time to develop a new and healthy habit. Give yourself the time you need.

## Perseverance

Wonderful and positive changes will occur with meditation. The most important thing you can do is keep practicing as often as you can. Stick with it, even if you feel that nothing's happening. There's always an unconscious, progressive impact. There are great health benefits in just coming to your meditation place no matter what you experience in that particular session.

## Patience

Meditation is a slow, progressive process that is always evolving. Don't expect an instant "aha!" after a short time. Be patient with your own progress. It can be frustrating when it seems that your mind is *always* wandering and *always* thinking. There will be times when you can't seem to concentrate on the object of your meditation. Can you remember when you first started to learn something new like how to play a musical instrument or a new sport, or when you first learned to drive? You weren't an expert overnight. It takes time to learn a new skill. Just know that if you spend enough time practicing, your concentration will improve.

## Presence

Simply be present to whatever occurs in your meditation experience. If you find yourself feeling frustration, anger, happiness, or sadness during the course of your meditation session, then just acknowledge, or recognize what you're feeling without trying to grab onto the emotion or engage it. Also, don't try to forcefully push the emotion away. Accept the presence of whatever occurs as it happens. Be aware of thoughts and feelings as they try to pull you into the past, or entice you into thoughts of the future. Return your focus to your breathing as soon as you're able. Refocusing on your breath-cycle will guide you back into the here and now.

## Perfection

You should not be concerned about whether the meditation practice that you're doing is 'perfect' or if you're doing it 'the right way'. You're doing an awesome job in just practicing. Try not to have unrealistic expectations about the way you think the meditation session should be going. The meditation that you're experiencing, at that point, is what exists for you in that moment. You're benefiting from the routine of meditating no matter what you experience in any given session.

Your meditation will be different every time. Sometimes it will be what you may perceive as a "good" meditation, other times it will be a more challenging experience. Try not to come to your meditation with an expectation that it will be 'good' like the last time. Come to your meditation with no expectations. As long as you're trying to meditate, you're doing just fine! Be kind to yourself.

### Promise

I promise you that the benefits you will get from meditation are invaluable. With time and practice you will experience this. If you can make meditation a priority, then it will become so important to you and your well-being, that you will always make time for it in your life. In the beginning, you may just have to trust that these benefits, which may not be so obvious to you initially, will gradually reveal themselves. Promise yourself that you will give meditation your best effort.

## Meditation Postures

There are several positions that you can take for meditation. The important thing is to choose one that feels comfortable for you. Over time, if you're generally choosing a sitting posture, your flexibility may increase and you can try other postures that you might have found to be uncomfortable when you first started. All the positions are equally good. Sitting on the floor is not better than sitting in a chair. Do whatever works best for you!

The list on the following pages will familiarize you with some of the phrases common to meditation, but pretzel-like contortions are not important. As long as you're maintaining a position that is stable and comfortable, you're on the right track.

### Sitting on the Floor

When sitting on the floor you should feel grounded and stable. You may find it helpful to have a mat or carpet to sit on. It's very important to have the *buttocks higher than the knees.* Try sitting on a cushion, to elevate your buttocks and allow *your pelvis to tilt forward*, creating a more comfortable curve in your lower back. Sit on the edge of the cushion, rather than in the middle of it, to encourage this forward pelvic tilt. Elevating the pelvis allows for greater stability as there are multiple points of contact between your legs and the floor.

If your knees are not both, or equally touching the floor, try *using a cushion to support the knee that doesn't touch*. This will take pressure off of your knees and legs and allow you to sit more comfortably.

Try to *practice the sitting posture whenever you can*. If you're sitting on a chair, or on a sofa, remember to assume the sitting position that you use when you're doing your meditation. The more often you sit in this position the more your ease and flexibility will increase, and you'll find the position to be more comfortable and less distracting during your meditation.

### The Butterfly Exercise

There are also hip exercises that you can do to increase your flexibility. The Butterfly exercise involves sitting on the floor with the knees bent sideways and the soles of the feet touching each other. Interlace your fingers and wrap your hands around your toes. Rhythmically lower and raise your knees, but don't bounce them, or force them. Remember that the motion should be gentle without overstretching or causing any pain.

## Sitting Postures

- **Cross-legged posture**
  The sides of both feet touch the floor and the legs are comfortably crossed.

- **Half-lotus**
  Sit cross-legged. The left foot is on the floor under the right leg and the right foot is on top of the left thigh.

- **Full-lotus**
  Sit cross-legged with each foot placed with the sole upward on the thigh of the opposite leg.

- **Bench**
  There is a special meditation bench that supports the weight of your body and allows your feet to be curled underneath.

- **Sitting on a chair**
  When sitting on a chair, try to sit more at the edge of it. Both feet should be flat on the floor. If your feet don't reach the floor comfortably you can fold a blanket for your feet to rest upon. Your back should be upright and not touching the back of the chair.

## Lying Down

If, for some reason, you have physical limitations such that the only comfortable posture for you is lying down, this can be done as well. However, this posture is not recommended for those who are physically able because of the tendency to fall asleep. In this posture, make sure to be comfortable but extra aware of the need to stay alert.

## Standing

Standing up to meditate can be very helpful when fatigue is becoming a problem in a sitting posture.

What you may find is that, by simply assuming the meditation posture, the posture itself starts to bring about a calming effect on your body. At first you may experiment with different postures to find the one that's right for you, but I recommend that, after a while, you settle on the one that you find the most comfortable.

## *What should the rest of your body be doing?*

- **Spine**
  Your spine should be straight and upright, but not rigid and tense.

- **Head-chin**

  Your head and chin should be held straight and facing forward or directed slightly downward. As your muscles get tired, it's common for your head to tilt forward. Sometimes drawing the head back slightly will keep the spine in the right alignment.

- **Eyes**

  It's usually best to close your eyes, unless you're doing a visual meditation, as you'll be less distracted. However, some people recommend that your eyes be slightly open with your gaze directed downward. Again, it's all about what works for you personally. Be comfortable and if you wear glasses you should remove them.

- **Tongue**

  Your tongue may lie relaxed, on the floor of your mouth. Another option is that the tip of your tongue may touch the roof of your mouth just behind the upper teeth.

- **Mouth**

  Your mouth should ideally be closed to help keep you breathing through your nose. If you find this difficult, like when you have a cold, then breathe through your mouth.

  Sit with a small *smile*. This will help relax your body and give some lightness to your practice.

- **Hands**

  Your hands may rest in your lap with the right hand on top of the left hand. Your palms should be facing upward and your hands should be slightly cupped. The tip of your thumbs should touch, but your hands should be fully relaxed.

  You may also fold your arms at your belly button. The right palm should be sitting over the left palm and the thumbs can be touching. Keeping the arms in this position creates some body tension that may be a reminder to keep your spine straight.

An alternative is for each hand to rest on your thighs just above your knees with your palms facing downward. The tip of your thumb and index finger should touch on each hand.

- **Arms**
Relax your arms so that they are held lightly against the sides of your body.

- **Shoulders**
Your shoulders should be relaxed, which means down and slightly back. Shrug your shoulders a few times before you begin to see if they are tensed upward or fully relaxed.

- **Chest**
Most people have a tendency, over time, to collapse forward. Elevating or throwing the chest outward helps to keep you upright.

- **Body**
It may be very helpful to maintain a feeling of *stillness* in the body. There should be no movement in the meditation posture. This physical stillness helps to create mental stillness.

Your body will have some comments to make about your new meditation practice. It might not like sitting still for that long. Some days will be better than others. Weak muscle groups will announce themselves and try to get you to move around or to even stop meditating entirely. Make yourself as comfortable as you can and if you have to move, then move! That's ok. However, if you move, do so slowly and with careful attention to what you're doing. With every meditation that you do, your body and mind will grow more accustomed to it and you'll feel less distracted and more and more comfortable. It only gets better!

## Your Meditation Environment

- **Lights**
  The lights should be off or dimmed and the curtains closed if you're meditating in daylight and finding it to be distractingly bright.

- **Shawl or blanket**
  As you meditate, your body's metabolic rate falls and with it, your body temperature. You may start to feel colder. Having a shawl or light blanket with you that you can put over your shoulders if you get cold may be helpful. If you find that you get cold often when you meditate, it may be better to wear a sweater, or shawl from the start.

- **Clothes**
  Wear loose comfortable clothes that don't interfere with diaphragmatic breathing.

- **Phone, TV, Radio, iPod**
  Turn them off. This is your time, don't share it.

Do try to make your meditation environment pleasant, peaceful and calming. It's your sanctuary while you're meditating, so try to anticipate any distractions and eliminate them as best you can before you begin. There will always, of course, be some distractions, and you'll learn to just be aware of them and then return your focus to your meditation. Don't hesitate to tell those that you live with that you're meditating (or doing your breathing exercises etc.) so that they can help to give you the time and peace that you need.

## *So, how do you meditate?*

There are many ways to meditate. In a *Concentration Practice* you'd choose one object and maintain a constant uninterrupted focus on that object the whole time. This "object" could actually be your breath, the movement of part of your body, a particular phrase, or even a light or sound. The following instructions use the breath as the meditation focus.

When you meditate you just need to remember to "**SAW.**"

**S** – Sit in the right position
**S** – Scan your body
**S** – Set the intention
**A** – be Aware of your breath
**W** – Watch your breathing

The following is a list of specific instructions to better inform your meditation practice. It's more important that you meditate any way you can, than that you get too caught up in specifics. Don't worry. You'll understand these instructions more once you've begun your practice:

1. Choose a *spot* for meditation that's quiet and has few distractions.
2. Choose a *length of time* and set a timer for that amount. Five to ten minutes is a great start.
3. Choose a position like sitting on a chair, or on the ground.
4. *Set* your body position. Sit in an upright, still and relaxed manner. A still body leads to a still mind.
5. Initially *scan the body* for any physical tension. Imagine your breath traveling from your toes to the top of your head, and from the top of your head back to your toes. If there's tension in one body part, stay focused on that part and imagine breathing in and out of the place of tension until that tension releases. Physical stillness and relaxation are important for mental relaxation.
6. *Ground* yourself in your body by bringing your attention to the physical sensations of your feet touching the floor and your buttocks touching your cushion, or chair. Focus on these physical sensations for several breaths.

7. *Set the intention for your practice.* You want to give your mind a task for it to do during your practice. Start by saying something to yourself like, *"May I have constant attention on my breath,"* or *"May I have uninterrupted mindfulness,"* or *"May my mind be quiet and still."*

8. Your *concentration point* is the place where you feel the breath most noticeably. Is it at:
   • the spot between your upper lip and the tip of the *nostrils*?
   • your *chest* as it rises and falls?
   • your *abdomen* as it rises and falls?
   • the *movement cycle* of the breath as it moves from the nostrils, through the chest to the abdomen and then back to the chest and out through the nostrils?
   • The spot between the upper lip and the tip of the nostrils may be the best location to focus your attention as it is a small area and that helps you concentrate.

9. *Breathe consciously* for at least five breath-cycles or as long as it feels comfortable. Keep your breathing smooth, even, deep, quiet, long, and don't forget to breathe diaphragmatically from the abdomen. Breathing *deeply* will fully expand the lungs and allow for easier breath movements.

10. *Emphasize the exhalation* or out-breath until there's no more air left to breathe out. Do this on the last breath of your five, conscious, deep breaths. Allow yourself to rest in the space between the end of the exhalation and the next inhalation, until your body spontaneously starts the next inhalation. Just experience what it feels like to allow yourself to be moved by the body as it breathes in and out automatically.

11. *Watch the breath.* Focus attention at the spot that you've selected in your body (your concentration point), such as at your nostrils, in your abdomen, or chest. Allow yourself to be moved spontaneously by the breath. You are not consciously controlling your breathing after your first five deep breaths.

12. Notice the *physical sensation* of the breath as it moves back and forth past your concentration point.

13. There are several techniques that you can use to maintain your concentration on your breath:
    - *Focus* your attention on the *qualities of the breath* as it moves past your place of concentration. How does the breath *feel* at that spot? Is it warm or cold? Regular or irregular? Deep or shallow? Continuous or discontinuous? Quiet or loud? Short or long? Effortless or forced? Do you feel that parts are vibrating, stretching or contracting? Does the feeling change over time?
    - Create the *attitude* that the breath is *very important*. Where would you be if you couldn't breathe? Be amazed at how your body works to automatically breathe. Cherish the movement of your breath. Do you have a passion for sports, art, music or entertainment? Can you bring the same focus and interest to your breath that you bring to your object of passion?
    - *Follow the breath-cycle* from the beginning to the end of the in-breath, and from the beginning to the end of the out-breath.
    - There are *pauses* between the in and out, and out and in-breaths. The pause between the end of exhalation and the beginning of the inhalation is the most obvious part of the complete breath-cycle. Rest your awareness in the stillness and silence of this pause at your *concentration point*. Notice what this pause, where there is no movement, feels like at the spot that you've chosen as your concentration point. This stillness will give you a taste of what your mind can be like when it's silent and still.
    - It can be difficult to let go of your conscious control of your breathing when you're meditating. You may find yourself interfering with the natural movements of the breath. Specifically bring your attention to the point where the lungs start to move out of the pause between inhalation and exhalation to counteract this tendency.
14. *Counting your breaths* is another excellent way to maintain your concentration on the breath. An in and out-breath is

one cycle. Count your in and out-breath cycles from one to ten and then back down again counting from ten to one. Keep counting until you feel that your concentration is solid and then stop counting as you continue to focus on your breathing. Sometimes you might find yourself having to count throughout the entire meditation. The counting should just be in the background and should not be the focus of your concentration. Your concentration should remain first and foremost on your breathing.

15. If you're more attuned to your sense of hearing, you may also use the *sound of your breath* as it moves in and out as your concentration point.

16. It can be difficult to maintain your concentration on the breath. Don't be surprised or upset if you find that you get caught up in thoughts, emotions and physical sensations. Once you become aware that you're no longer focused on your breathing, just bring your attention back to your breath. *Don't criticize or judge yourself.*

17. Sometimes your thoughts, emotions and physical sensations can be very powerful. This is where mindfulness really helps. Bring awareness to the thought, emotion or sensation without judgment and reactivity. Be present to what is without wanting to change it or identifying with it. When a strong thought, emotion, or physical sensation arises, *label* it with terms such as "thinking," "sadness," "anger," "twisting feeling," "burning sensation" etc. You will often experience thoughts and emotions as a physical sensation. Try to experience the physicality of the thought or emotion, and then bring yourself back to focusing on your breath.

## Vipassana Meditation

Another form of meditation is called *Vipassana* or *Insight Meditation*. In this technique, you're resting in the awareness of whatever presents itself instead of trying to focus on one specific object such as your breath. You are observing everything that's going on mentally and physically, without trying to change anything.

The setup for this meditation is exactly the same as the concentration practice. It can be helpful to follow the breath in the beginning to settle your mind. Once you feel settled, rest in the awareness of whatever presents itself. If there's a throbbing sensation in your knee, experience that. If there's a thought or emotion that pops up, rest in the awareness of that thought or emotion. Whatever the dominant sensation is, relax and focus on it until the next sensation comes along.

In the beginning, it can be helpful to label each sensation as it emerges into your conscious awareness. If your mind is resting too much in fantasy, it may help to focus once again on your breathing until your mind is stabilized again.

This is a wonderful way to practice a mindfulness of all sensations and to see the impermanence of all experience.

## Walking Meditation

You can meditate in almost any situation, lying down, sitting or even walking. In a walking meditation you use the physical movement of your body as the object of your concentration and mindfulness. You bring your awareness to every physical sensation that occurs while walking. This is an excellent alternative to sitting in meditation, as in a sitting posture sometimes fatigue sets in when your body is still for a long time.

To perform a walking meditation, you will need a space that is uncluttered. This space should be large enough that you can take ten steps in a straight line. To start, stand at one end of the room, with your back straight.

Focus your attention on your feet and notice how they feel against the ground. Slowly lift one leg, feeling how the muscles contract and how your whole body changes as it's balancing in response to this action. Notice how your other leg has contracted to maintain your balance. Slowly move your raised leg to take a step and mindfully note the second when your raised heel makes contact with the ground. Begin to add your weight to the step and slowly feel the changes in your body as this new balance is accommodated. Continue to slowly take steps across the room while trying to notice every little aspect of your body as it moves through the steps.

Feel the sensations of movement and the point of contact between your feet and the ground. See how each step is unique. Look for how the sensations are constantly changing as a way of maintaining your uninterrupted attention and interest. When you reach the other end of the room, turn and repeat the process as you continue to walk back and forth.

In a modification of the above process, you can bring your awareness to the *intent to move* that is present, before you actually move your body. Before any movement, or speech is carried out, your mind creates the intent to perform it in your consciousness. If you bring your attention to what happens before you speak or move, you can hear the words before they are spoken, and experience the urge to move before any movement occurs. Try to bring your awareness to the intent to move, before you take each step of your walking meditation.

You can also try to *coordinate the movement of the breath with the movement of the body*. For example with an inhalation you lift one leg and with an exhalation you then place the foot on the ground. If you are moving faster you may lift and place your foot with an inhalation. With an exhalation you then lift and place the other foot on the ground. You can discover whatever rhythm of breathing, coordinated with movement, works best for you. This is a way to maintain your concentration on your breathing by using physical movement to help support your focus.

As a formal practice you can set aside five to ten minutes a day, or longer, for a walking meditation. Performed mindfully, it's a wonderful way to relax and concentrate your mind.

You can also practice a walking meditation informally. Whenever you're walking somewhere in your daily life, try to bring your attention, mindfully to the act of walking. This will connect you to the present moment and promote relaxation.

# Meditation Pitfalls, Hurdles, Trips and Traps

## Physical Discomfort

It's not uncommon for you to experience some physical discomfort, even minor pain, when first starting to meditate. Your body is probably going to complain. It's going to want to itch and squirm and move. This may reflect a release of stored tension within your body that only becomes evident as you slow your mind down. It may indicate that your muscles are a bit tight and are simply not used to sitting in the posture you've chosen. The more you meditate, the easier it will be for you to sit still. Practice stretching exercises for your hips, such as the Butterfly exercise discussed in the Sitting Posture section of this chapter. When possible, assume your meditation posture throughout the day, such as when watching TV or reading a book.

When discomfort, pain or itching first starts, use it as the object of your concentration. Instead of calling it pain, try to think of what you're feeling as just another physical sensation. Explore what the pain really feels like. Is it twisting, burning, grabbing or sharp? Is it constant or does it fluctuate? What does your mind say about the pain? Do you feel any fear regarding it? If the pain begins to be overwhelming, or is becoming significant, it's perfectly okay to move, but try to move in a slow and mindful way. Once the pain has resolved, you can then resume your normal meditation posture.

## Sleepiness

If you really feel lethargic and sleepy during meditation this may reflect that you're actually sleep deprived. Getting more sleep is essential and is yet another way to improve your response to everyday stress. Everything is tougher when you're sleepy. Just as a young child is grouchy and emotional when tired, so are you, but you probably hide it a little better.

If you find yourself nodding off during your meditation, initially check that you're holding your spine in an upright but relaxed position. Make sure that your head is not bending forward as your chin tries to sneak toward your chest. Often, when you become tired, your posture is not maintained and this is the first clue that you're beginning to get fatigued.

Try opening your eyes.

You could also try standing up and meditating in a standing position.

Another option, that I've already mentioned, is the Walking Meditation, wherein you keep your attention on your breath as you slowly walk around the room.

You can give yourself a quick wakeup anytime by grasping your ear lobe and giving it a good squeeze.

Consider that your environment may also be contributing to your sleepiness.

Allow more light into the room.

Try meditating at a different time of day when you're not as vulnerable to fatigue.

If none of these suggestions seem to work for you, then maybe you're just really tired and you need some rest. Sometimes the simplest solutions are the best. Try catching a nap during the day and recognize that there will be some days when you're just plain tired. It's okay. Tomorrow is another day!

## Restlessness

You can also experience the opposite of sleepiness, which can manifest itself as a sense of restlessness in your mind or body.

To deal with this restlessness, try to increase your concentration on your breathing. Try counting each breath, like counting sheep. Count one as you breathe in and out, two for the next breath in and out until you reach ten. Then count back from ten to one.

Exhalation helps to promote relaxation, while inhalation tends to be energizing. Emphasizing exhalation by trying to breathe out longer than you breathe in can also help with restlessness. Breathe in and count the time it takes to fill your lungs, then try to take longer to completely breathe out. Try to empty your lungs as much as is comfortable.

## Doubt

As people first start to meditate, they may become frustrated and wonder whether it's really all that valuable to them. They have doubts about whether it's worth it or they may think it's just not working for them. They question if they are doing it right or enough. They have self-doubts and sabotage their own efforts by saying they don't have time, or they can't sit still or concentrate etc. These doubts are to be expected. Please don't let them stop you. It's important to give meditation time. You're not alone. Simply trust the wisdom of all the people that have gone before you and who have meditated and found it to be of real value. It's an excellent means of relaxation and stress relief. Give it a really good try and if you lose the habit, try again. Keep trying. Your health is worth it!

## Altered Images and Sensations

It's not uncommon for people to experience strange sensations in the mind or body while meditating. This just reflects the mind adjusting to the meditation. Meditation is a wonderful practice where you can achieve a state of deep concentration and stillness. There is nothing mysterious or magical about it. If you have a committed practice you can obtain peace of mind, stress release and a calm presence. It's worth the effort! But it requires perseverance and a dedicated commitment.

# Practice

Set up your meditation practice, keeping in mind the suggestions given here. Commit to doing it every day for at least a month. Ideally, it will become a permanent part of your healthy lifestyle. Remember that it takes time for a new habit to become...well...a habit!

## Summary

- Meditation is the action of focusing your attention on one object in order to reach a state of concentration and stillness.
- Your thoughts affect your body, so if you relax your mind by causing it to concentrate on something, you are relaxing your body and giving yourself an excellent break from stress.
- Mindfulness Meditation allows you to practice observing your thoughts without reacting to them. This practice will help you to become less reactive to your thoughts and their storylines when you're not meditating.
- When you meditate you just need to remember to "**SAW**," which means to **S**it in the right position, **S**can your body, **S**et the intention, be **A**ware of your breath, and **W**atch your breathing.
- How to meditate: Choose a quiet place. Set a timer for a predetermined amount of time such as ten to fifteen minutes to start. Choose a position, for example, sitting on the floor or a chair. Choose something to focus your awareness on, such as your breathing. Focus and refocus your attention as it wanders, bringing it back again and again to the object of your focus.
- It's quite common for people to experience some physical discomfort, sleepiness, doubt or unusual sensations, or images, when first starting to meditate, but it's important for you to stick with it and allow the benefits to gradually build for you.

# 12

# Mindfulness in Action: Being Present in the Moment

THIS CHAPTER WILL REALLY GIVE YOU a good grounding in how to make mindfulness a part of your life. The more you can integrate these suggestions into how you live from day to day, the less stress you'll carry around like an elephant on your back.

Let's further explore the concept of being present to the moment. Surprisingly, you probably frequently miss out on a lot of what's happening in your life. You may eat your food, but not taste it because you're reading the newspaper or watching TV. You may be on holidays, but not really enjoy the sun because your mind is back home thinking about work. Even if you're engaged in a conversation with a friend, you may not really hear him or her because you're busy thinking about what you're going to say next, rather than intently listening to the other person.

The nature of the human mind is that it often lacks the concentration to be fully present to what's currently going on. However, you can train your mind to learn how to focus on the moment. Here's more about how you can do just that!

## Living with Mindfulness

### Now is the Only Real Moment

The first thing you should recognize is how valuable it is for you to learn to be more present to what's going on. Past events are gone and future events haven't happened. The only *real moment* that exists is what's happening right now.

## This Moment is Precious

Anyone can die in an instant. Every moment is valuable and precious. Once it has passed, it's gone forever and you can't reclaim it. Ask yourself, *"How would I enjoy this moment if I only had 24 hours to live?"* Even if you find yourself dealing with a difficult problem, there's still just this present moment to experience. This very moment should be viewed as even more precious than other moments, as when you think of it that way, it gives you a break from your regularly scheduled programming of much scarier or upsetting thoughts.

To emphasize the preciousness of this moment and the fact that you have the ability to enjoy it, think of other people who are less fortunate than you. This could be personal friends, family, or even acquaintances that have suffered emotional or physical challenges. You might briefly reflect on the tragedies that the homeless people in your city suffer, or the people of the world who face civil war and natural disasters such as earthquakes or flooding. Let go of these more depressing thoughts and realize that where you are right now, in this moment, is truly not so bad. It's actually pretty good. Look at it that way!

## How to Be in the Moment

Bring *awareness* to what you're doing. If you're not aware of what's happening in the present moment, there's no way you can practice mindfulness.

- **Name your activity**

  Whenever you remember to, *name* or *label* to yourself, whatever activity you're doing. This helps you to be more interested and aware of what you're doing and to better concentrate on it. For example, you may say to yourself something like, "Now eating," "Now walking," "Now washing my hands" etc. just as you practiced labeling thoughts, feelings, and sensations in previous chapters.

- **Maintain concentration**
  One of the problems that people who are first practicing mindfulness report is that they have not developed the attribute of *sustained concentration* in order to really pay attention to whatever they're doing. The human mind is like a butterfly flitting from one sensation to another. Try to consciously maintain your concentration on what you're doing and guess what? You'll get better at it! No one expects you to be stressed out one day and mindful and calm the next. It's a process. Whatever you can do in your life to be more mindful is a step in the right direction.

- **Look less, see more!**
  *Slow down* your activity. This will allow you to have more time to fully experience it. It's also easier to focus your attention if you take your time. Try to look less and see more.

- **Create interest**
  Your mind can become bored fairly easily and is usually on the lookout for the next sensation. You can create greater *interest* in any given moment by asking yourself, "*What's new or special about this experience?*"

  You can also try to look at things more actively rather than passively. Rather than just looking at a bunch of trees and thinking, "a forest," slow down, take the time and interest, to look more closely at the trees that make up the forest. Observe how the forest is really many trees and that each one is distinct. Notice how the trees blow in the wind and how the leaves flutter on the branches. There's a tremendous beauty in the parts that make up the whole and then in the whole itself, once all the parts are reintegrated. Start looking for that beauty more often.

- **Find joy**
  Approach each moment from a place of *joy*. If you have a choice (and you do!) it's certainly better to go through life from a

place of joy rather than sadness. In each moment ask yourself, *"What's joyous about this moment?"* Don't just wait for joy to come and find you by accident. Go looking for it!

- **Practice gratitude**
  Come to each moment from a place of *gratitude*. For example, when eating your food, be grateful for nature reflected in the sun, earth, rain, and seeds that allowed the food to grow. Be thankful that you had the money to buy this food. Appreciate that you may be physically well enough that you have an appetite, you can feed yourself, you can swallow your food and you can digest your food to whatever degree is possible for you. Mika reminds herself regularly how grateful she is to have a life here in Canada and a job where she can provide for her family. Look for a reason to be thankful and encourage this attitude of gratitude whenever you can.

- **Be playful**
  Allow the child within you to come alive in each moment. There's a tremendous delight to be found in enjoying a moment from a joyful, curious, spontaneous, *child-like* perspective. Let yourself be present to the playful nature within you. If you're walking in the forest and suddenly want to walk balancing on top of a log, do it. If you want to skip stones in a pond, do it! Indulge yourself once in a while. Have fun!

- **Quiet your mind**
  You have to get out of your own head a bit, in order to overcome the habit of judging all of your experiences. Quiet your mind and come to your experiences from a place of relative mental *silence*. This will help you to fully appreciate each moment. When you bring your attention to something of interest, use this as an opportunity to initially take a deep breath in and out. This will help you to calm your body and mind, so that you may be more relaxed in the moment and can then really take in something that interests you, fully and completely.

- **Be more open**
Be present from an *openness of heart and mind*. Allow yourself to *feel* what you're experiencing. Put aside your judgments and preconceived ideas. Be receptive to new ideas, new people, new situations, and new concepts. Let the world in!

- **Smile!**
Put a *smile* on your face when encountering life. My patient Larry looks like a pretty scary guy when you first meet him, but when he smiles, it changes his whole appearance and people react to him in a totally different way. Research has found that the physical act of smiling, even when you don't feel like it very much, will lift your spirit.

## Remind Yourself to Be Mindful

You may approach each day with the best of intentions, but you'll find that even though you know that mindfulness is really good for you, you'll still forget to be mindful. People often tell me, "I would be mindful if I could only remember!" Here are some suggestions to help you to remember to be mindful.

- As I mentioned many times before, I am a fan of *Post-It* notes. Stuck in convenient places, they are great reminders. They may have messages on them such as, "Are you being mindful?" You could put one on the fridge that says, "Don't forget to be mindful when you eat." You could put one in the bathroom near the faucet that says, "Be mindful while washing your hands."
- Put reminders to yourself on *Facebook* so that you're mindful when checking in.
- Put a reminder on your *computer desktop* or *smart phone*, basically anywhere that you think will work for you.
- Choose an *environmental cue* that will be your constant reminder to be mindful when doing that activity. It could be the ring tone on your phone, whenever you have a cup of

tea or coffee, when you make dinner, when a TV commercial comes on, when you shave etc.

- Use a watch, phone or laptop with an *alarm* that you've set for every one, two or three hours to be your reminder and then take a moment to pay attention to the present as mindfully as possible when the alarm goes off.

- Tell *friends* what you're up to and ask them to text, tweet, message, or email you the occasional reminder. Ask them to send a suggestion about what you could be particularly mindful of that day. Your friends or family can be a wonderful source of support and encouragement as you incorporate mindfulness into your life.

- Create resolve by regularly acknowledging your *intention* to practice mindfulness. You can say to yourself, "*May I be mindful all the time.*" Interestingly, your mind takes this suggestion and will continue to work on it subconsciously, which will help you to be mindful more often. Whenever you remember, repeat to yourself, your formal intention to be mindful.

- Try to use the moment when your mind has formulated an *intention to act* as a cue to practice mindfulness. Before you speak or move, you have a moment before the words or action, when you already have in mind the intention to perform the activity. By constantly bringing your attention to this moment you will develop your practice of mindfulness.

- Whenever you're mindful of any action, use that as a cue to *bring mindfulness to your breath*. As you know, the act of observing, deepening, and lengthening the breath is the best technique for stress relief.

- The more you *practice mindfulness*, the more you create the momentum that reinforces further mindfulness.

- Whenever there is a change in the nature of your activities during your busy day, try to make use of these *transition points* as reminders to be more mindful.

### What now?

It's easier to be mindful when a strong thought, emotion or physical sensation is present. However, often you'll be in a mental and/or emotional state without necessarily being conscious of it. This state might just be in the background of your activities without calling for your attention.

The body can often be the indirect clue to what you are unconsciously experiencing. It can be helpful during your day to stop and just scan the body and feel if there's any tension anywhere. When I personally do this, sometimes I feel some contraction in the abdomen. I always investigate further by inquiring, *"What's going on right now?"* What often arises is some underlying anxiety, such as a drive to accomplish something. I am not even aware of this underlying tension until I consciously bring my awareness to my body. Recognizing the tension, I can rest with mindfulness in the mental and physical sensations using a focus on my breathing to support the relaxation and acceptance of what's present.

# Practice

First and foremost in the practice of mindfulness, fully experience whatever you're doing. Here are a couple of exercises that help you to really focus on your activity in a mindful fashion.

## Eating Mindfully

I'll use eating as an example of how you can be truly present to the activity you're engaged in. Frequently, when you eat, you may find yourself doing other things at the same time, such as talking, reading or watching TV. The next time you eat a meal, I'd like you to try an experiment. Only eat. Don't surf the Net, listen to your iPod, talk, or read. Try to become fully present to the act of eating from the beginning to the end of the meal. This is how you'd go about eating a meal mindfully and I'd like you to try it.

As you start to eat, observe what your intention is in eating. Are you eating because you're hungry, because you're angry, or sad and you're using food as a way to soothe yourself, or because it's just dinnertime and yet you're not hungry? Watch how your mind chooses the particular food on the plate, how much it chooses and how it tells your hand to collect the food on the fork, or spoon. Observe the process of how you bring the food to your mouth, the saliva that starts to accumulate in your mouth and how you swallow the food.

Do you want to pick up another morsel of food before you have even finished the first bite? And why is that?

Try to put the fork or spoon down after you put the food in your mouth and simply observe the sensations that arise. What's its texture, its smell, its taste?

Then, when you have swallowed it, proceed with eating more. When do you stop eating? When all the food on the plate is gone or when you feel full?

If you decide to eat a second helping, ask yourself why you did that. If the answer that pops up is, "Because I felt like it," don't let your inquiry stop there. Is it because you're truly hungry, or do you feel that you need to take as much food as you can to fill some other need? Remember, you're investigating yourself.

By slowing down and observing this process, you will have been truly present to the experience of eating. Not only will you enjoy your sensations that much more, but you'll begin to see how your mind operates and makes the choices it does without really consulting you.

## Showering Mindfully

The next time you take a shower, I'd like you to do it mindfully as well. Again, try to be present to the actual sensations of the event, but also carefully observe how your mind makes its decisions.

When you take a shower, observe how your mind has created a ritual about this event. Why are you taking the shower? Are you dirty? Does it provide physical and emotional comfort? Is it simply the time of day that you normally take a shower? Do you start the shower first and let the water get warm and then get undressed? Do you position your towel or your hair products in a certain place? Do you wash your hair or your body first? Do you start with the left or right side? Do you start with the upper or lower body? Do you rinse off your head or your body first?

Notice the sensations. How does it feel to have the water hit your body? Notice the sensation of your hands rubbing the soap and shampoo on you; the feeling of the towel drying you when the shower is finished.

There are a lot of decisions that go into the routine act of taking a shower! When does your mind make the decision that you've been in the shower long enough? When you're in the shower, are you mentally present or somewhere else entirely, such as already at work, eating breakfast, or thinking about the weekend? When the shower is done, how do you feel?

You can see from these examples how your mind is constantly making moment-to-moment decisions that impact how you engage the world. Mindfulness encompasses the actual sensations of the experience, how your mind processes it and how it makes decisions throughout.

Every week, choose one activity that you do, that you will now deliberately do mindfully, with your full attention. This could be whenever you shower, make your peanut-butter sandwich, eat your fruit, go to the bathroom etc. Start to think about how and why you make the decisions that you do and be present to the sensations that arise in the moment.

## Summary

- You frequently miss out on a lot of what's happening in your life by not focusing your mind on the present moment.
- Focusing on anything other than what's happening right now is a major source of stress for most people.
- You can train your mind to learn how to focus on the moment.
- To integrate mindfulness into your life you need to practice it as much as possible.
- Living mindfully includes, focusing on right now, creating the intent to be mindful, maintaining improved concentration,

slowing down, creating interest, looking for the joy in things, practicing a grateful attitude, being playful and more open, quieting your mind, smiling more and reminding yourself to be mindful.

- Be present to the sensations that arise in the moment with an open and accepting attitude.

# 13
# The Mindful Mind

## Perception is Deception

**W**E ALL HAVE MINDS THAT ARE very judgmental and comparative. Everything you experience is judged and referenced against your own personal internal standards. When you see another person your mind automatically and instantly evaluates him or her. You probably don't tend to just greet that person with acceptance and openness, although it's perfectly normal to compare and judge. Your mind is unconsciously asking, "*Is that person acting in a way that fits with my internal belief system?*" "*Does he or she seem to have more, or appear better than me?*" and "*Am I safe?*" The stories you create about everything you encounter determine how you'll react.

You experience life by *referencing everything to yourself.* In addition, you have a sticky *velcro mind* when it comes to your own experiences. Of course you are the center of your own world, but a lot of your stress comes from this tendency to judge. If you can consciously perceive life through a perspective that is not quite so self-referential, you can get around your own habitual patterns of judgment. Think of it as experiencing life with a non-sticky *teflon mind.* You are then present to what you are experiencing without "sticking" to it by getting caught up in all the judgments and comparisons.

The idea is to create interest in whatever you perceive, in other words, to be *actively external* or *other directed.* Whatever or whomever you encounter, make a conscious and deliberate attempt to bring to the experience an attitude of interest and curiosity. If you ask your mind, "*What's interesting in this moment?*" or better still, *"What's extraordinary in this moment?"* your mind will be engaged in examining what's being experienced rather than self-referencing it. Bring mindfulness to the moment by being present to what is, rather than telling stories about it.

You particularly tend to judge other people. This is because your inner child does not normally view nature and buildings and so forth as a significant threat. It's important to recognize that everyone shares the same human condition as you do, with all its hopes and fears. Because of this, you're fundamentally and profoundly connected to them. Other people can be a constant reminder of your own humanity.

We all have an inner child, with its core-wounding, or emotionally damaging, childhood experiences, as well as our fair share of ongoing adult stressors that directly influence our behaviours. It can be helpful to remember that, although someone's actions may not seem appropriate, that person is driven by his or her own unmet needs and fears, just like you.

If you knew a person's history, you'd likely have more sympathy for that individual's behaviour. You might even realize that you would probably be doing exactly what that person is doing, if given the same circumstances. I have learned so much from my patients about compassion. They may present initially in a way that seems angry or distant, but once I learn their stories, I can understand why they are the way they are.

Mika first came to my office complaining of a long-standing history of abdominal pain, nausea, headaches, sleep disorders and fatigue. Multiple investigations over the years had been negative. She couldn't understand why the medical profession could not solve her problems. As we explored her history, she revealed that she had suffered physical and sexual abuse as a five-year-old child back in Thailand. She carried this legacy throughout her life. Her medical symptoms were a physical expression of her childhood traumas, as well as the ongoing stress of living and working in a new country.

When my patient Larry first came to my office, he was initially very uptight and angry. He had abdominal pain and bowel problems. My initial reaction to his angry demeanor was to be defensive, but slowly as the conversation unfolded and I explored what was going on in his life, he shared that he had been looking after his father for many years. His father had multiple medical issues and had died recently. What became apparent was that Larry was scared of suffering the same fate as his father and was worried that his symptoms could reflect an underlying serious medical problem. His anger was really a manifestation of his underlying fear. As Larry slowly shared his story with me, his anger softened. When I could explain the nature of his symptoms to him and reassure him, his spirits lifted and he became very pleasant and grateful.

You don't know the stories of the people you meet, but what's for sure is that everyone has a story. Some are more dramatic than others. Whenever you meet someone, ask yourself, *"What's this person's story?"* just to remind yourself that there may be some pain and past trauma that this person carries in his or her heart that influences how that person behaves in this world. If you knew that person's story you would probably feel a stronger sense of compassion for him or her. Imagine when you meet new people that you already have a connection with them. It will help you to be more open and accepting of them until you really do get to know them.

## Practice

1. Find a *picture* of yourself as a child. When you look at someone else, remember your own picture and let it be a reminder that the other person too has an inner child who's looking for love, acceptance, and safety. Naturally, in order to be treated well by other people, you need to treat other people the same way. The idea here is to try to get out of your own inner personal perspective and connect with people from a place of shared humanity.

   If you begin to focus more on similarities rather than differences, you will be able to be more understanding and *compassionate*. When you can start to treat other people more compassionately, you may also start to treat yourself with more compassion as well. More compassion means less stress.

2. Throughout your day, try to actively treat people with more compassion. Work on being kinder to those around you.

## Summary

- If you can view life through an external rather than an internal self-referencing perspective, there will be less of a tendency for your mind to judge.
- It's important to connect with people from a place of shared humanity instead of from an inner judgmental, self-directed perspective.
- Compassion for others leads you to be more compassionate with yourself, which will mean less stress in your life.

# 14

## Other Techniques for Stress Management

### Focus on Another Thought

**Y**OUR THOUGHTS ARE VERY POWERFUL and once you get caught up in one of your stories you often get lost in it for a while. You can try to distract yourself by *refocusing your attention on another thought*. Try to bring your attention to one of your favourite holiday places, write a shopping list, or recite a prayer or poem. Even try solving a crossword puzzle to remove yourself from the clutches of your own story. A bit of distraction can sometimes give you that little morsel of distance that you need in order to come to your thoughts or problems more mindfully.

### Focus on the Dominant Word in the Thought

Another interesting technique that you can use when stressed, is to continue to *repeat the dominant word in the story* that your mind is telling you in response to stress-filled thoughts. You may have done something and, as a result, your mind is telling you that you're stupid, terrible, or foolish. You would then continue to repeat one of these words, for example, "terrible," over and over again, until all that you're left with is the act of repeating the word, without any of the feelings that originally went along with the story.

The story loses its power, as you become focused on the word. The word "terrible" becomes just an empty sound without the associated energy of the rest of your inner commentary. By using this technique, you're short-circuiting the story and your mind will move on to something else. It really becomes evident, with this technique, how temporary your thoughts actually are.

## Use "What's Next?"

Your mind constantly evaluates everything you encounter. However, can you really know what your next thought is going to be? Interestingly, when you bring your attention specifically to the act of looking for what your next thought will be, your mind stops or slows down its chatter.

Try this experiment.

 Find your timer and set it for two minutes. Close your eyes and deliberately look for what your next thought will be. Rest in the stillness as you wait for the answer.

What did you notice? As you bring your focus to your own thought process, your mind tends to settle down.

You can use this technique whenever you encounter a sensation such as seeing a new person. If you see a stranger walking toward you, before your mind criticizes, compares and judges, ask yourself, *"What's next?"* Bring your attention to what your mind is going to say about what you have just experienced. You will find that your mind is less likely to now evaluate this stranger. This will allow you to experience what is, as it is, rather than through the filter of your mind's stories. This is the wonderful benefit of the light of awareness.

## Feed the Fire

Feeding the Fire is another technique that you can use when your mind is being self-critical, blaming and angry. Poor Mika had forgotten her friend's birthday and her mind was saying, "You're so thoughtless, stupid and horrible. How could you have forgotten your best friend's birthday?" Mika can better realize the exaggerated nature of her self-criticisms if she feeds the fire of negative comments by allowing them to become more extreme and unrealistic. She could intentionally worsen the content of her inner-commentary to make it more and more outlandish and ridiculous under the circumstances. She could say things to herself like:

> *You're the worst person in the world. What you did was horrible. You don't deserve to have any friends at all!*

There is a part inside of Mika that knows that these increasingly ridiculous thoughts are untrue. By intentionally worsening the content of your self-criticism, you will quickly see that it's untrue and often unfounded. Exercise a degree of caution with this technique. The idea is to exaggerate your critical thoughts so that you can see them as false and even silly, not to spiral down into greater depths of self-criticism and depression. As you become more confident in your ability to stand back and observe your thoughts from a place of stability and strength, then you may find this technique to be of value.

## Reframe The Situation

Another valuable tool in your fight against stress is the technique of *Reframing*. Reframing is the process by which you look at a situation from another point of view (i.e., from a different frame of mind, hence the term). This technique goes well with the practice of mindfulness and it should be used whenever possible. In times of stress, you really do need all the help you can get, so use everything you've got in order to get through.

Once you have seen how a story is created from the initial perception or sensation, the next step is to address the validity of your mind's assessment. Take a moment, when you become aware of a stream of thought and a storyline, to think about whether the story that you're telling yourself is true, helpful, or wise? Usually, whatever arises in your mind you take to be true. However, this assumption, that whatever you think is automatically true, is not valid or even helpful.

As we've discussed before, your thoughts reflect your conditioned belief system and that is specific to you personally. There are many ways to look at a situation. For example, where I live it snows frequently. When it does, a skier might say, "*This is great; I can go skiing!*" The non-skier might say, "*This is terrible; all this snow makes it too difficult to drive!*" Everybody has his or her own story to tell about any given event.

Unfortunately, the reactive stories that your mind comes up with are often extreme and unbalanced and usually predict some sort of catastrophe. Catastrophizing is what people do when they make mountains out of molehills, predict the worst possible outcome of any situation and generally believe it all to be a foregone conclusion, i.e., "*It's going to happen. I'm doomed.*"

To begin to reframe a situation from doom and gloom to a more realistic appraisal, it's helpful to write these scary thoughts down. Later, you will be able to go through the reframing process in your mind and may only need to resort to writing things down with particularly persistent thoughts.

Think about a distressing situation and listen to the statements that you are telling yourself about it. Make three vertical columns on a sheet of paper and in the first column write down these statements as best you can. Write, "*Is this true?*" at the top of the second column and at the top of the third write, "*Is there another way to look at it?*" Fill in the columns beside each statement. Just the exercise of bringing these thoughts into the light of day will help you to reframe the situation.

Writing your inner thoughts down puts you into the position of the observer. When you can pause and examine what you are really saying to yourself, what follows may be a sense that these statements, comments and criticisms are most likely unfair and untrue.

Going back to Mika and the time that she forgot her friend's birthday as an example, when Mika's friend mentioned that she had just celebrated her birthday, Mika went into hyper, self-critical mode:

*How could you have forgotten her birthday? You're the most thoughtless, inconsiderate and terrible person in the world. She will never be your friend again!*

These are pretty powerful, critical and angry thoughts. In response to her thoughts and their emotionally draining storyline, Mika felt tremendously sad, guilty and frightened. After her conversation with her friend, Mika decided to use the technique of reframing to reduce her sense of stress in the situation. She divided a piece of paper into three columns. In the first column she entered the thoughts that she was having about the situation. These questions and statements really captured the essence of what was happening in the moment for her.

Next Mika looked at each thought that she'd written down and asked herself, *"Is this true?"*

It's important to realize that the stories you often tell yourself are only the biased, unbalanced and extreme assessments of situations. The worst-case scenarios seldom come to pass and when they do, they are often not as bad as you thought they would be.

Are you really a thoughtless, inconsiderate and terrible person or did you just forget something? Will your friend never talk to you again, or will she be hurt but forgive you? Watch for the tendency to over-generalize. If it sounds extreme, it probably is.

Another way to look at this is to ask yourself, *"What would you say to a friend who was in a similar situation?"* Mika considered this question and then she wrote in column two on her sheet of paper a response to *"Is this true?"* beside her original statement.

*No, I am not a terrible person. I have always remembered her birthday in the past. I am a good friend to her. I listen to her when she has problems. She can usually count on me. I just made a mistake.*

Finally, Mika asked herself, *"Is there another way to look at this?"* What came up for her was:

*I did forget her birthday. People aren't always perfect. We all make mistakes. This was not intentional. I am still a good friend.*

She wrote this down in column three and began to feel her stress ease as she reframed the episode.

Even if you are not in a position to write your thoughts down you can still begin the reframing process in your mind and continue with the writing exercise later. Notice a stress-filled thought. Ask yourself, *"Is this true?"* and *"Is there another way to look at this?"*

Consider another example. In this instance, Mika had bought a necklace and her mind started to say, *"How could you have bought that necklace? It's so expensive! If you keep doing this you will be bankrupt. You're so irresponsible."* These were some pretty strong words for just buying a piece of jewelry!

Mika recognized that she was starting to get quite upset and in that moment she asked herself, *"Is this true?"* What came up was, *"Will I really go bankrupt if I buy this necklace? I have bought other expensive things before, for myself and my family, without any problems. I work hard. I have a good job and I think I can afford it."*

Continuing through to the last phase of reframing, Mika asked, *"Is there another way to look at this?"* The answer that arose for her was, *"I am not frivolous. I don't often buy myself anything. I really like what I bought. I will really enjoy it and wear it a lot."*

By examining the validity of the her self-critical comments, Mika was able to  bring some perspective, reality and balance to her situations. You too can practice reframing, both in a stressful moment as well as afterward when you have time to reflect and write things down. Reframing is a continuous process of examining whether your story about a situation is true or not and then trying to look at the situation from another perspective. You'll get better and better at it and it will really help to reduce your stress levels.

## Look for the Intent Behind Your Behaviour

Your mind can be very hard on you. With all of its judgments, it often has you believing that you're acting in a "bad" way. One way to counteract this is to ask your mind, "*What was the real intent behind my behaviour?*" When you can ask yourself if you intentionally acted in a way that was mean, insensitive, or cruel; or if your behaviour was actually coming from a place of good intention, caring and kindness; then you can counteract the unrealistic judging mind and be more accepting of yourself. If your motives are pure and not meant to hurt anyone then you can be more accepting of the outcome of your behaviour.

## Practice Equanimity

Equanimity is the characteristic of being calm and steady under stress. It just refers to accepting things for what they are. Events have occurred in your life that you may not be entirely happy with. The event could have occurred ten years ago or ten seconds ago. You probably have the tendency to still get upset over the event and dwell on it. You may find yourself going over and over the event in your mind, chastising yourself for what you did or didn't do, how stupid you were, asking how could you have done such a thing etc. However, these reruns of negative life episodes are not usually helpful in any way. Worrying about and replaying an event is not a time machine and has never successfully altered what has already happened. It is what it is. All you can do is try to move forward, from this point onward, with greater clarity and wisdom.

In an attempt to break your own patterns of response, it may be helpful during stressful times to ask:

- *"Can I change what has already happened in the past?"*
- *"Does worrying help the situation in any way?"*

When you recognize and accept that what has happened can't be changed, it starts to help you to release some of the frustration and anxiety that comes from replaying the event over and over again. Trust yourself that you made the best decision that you could have made, given who you were at that point in time. Show compassion for yourself and know that because of this event you're different now. You now have the ability to move past what has gone on previously and make the best decisions going forward. This will allow you to deal with your stress in the best state of mind possible under the circumstances.

The characteristic of equanimity is cultivated by two more questions that you should ask yourself in times of stress:

- *"What can I do, at this point in time, to best deal with the situation?"*
- *"What needs to be done?"*

When you use this second method of phrasing a question, in the middle of a crisis, it creates some distance from the self, the 'you' that is experiencing the stress, and just asks your mind to propose a solution to a problem. You're then able to access the greater wealth of intuitive wisdom that you have, that goes beyond the self-centered needs of your own inner child. Doing so will actually allow you to truly act in your own best interest during times of extreme stress.

## It's Just Your Nature

You are no different than an animal in the sense that you have a primal urge to be safe. You are programmed from the beginning of time to be aware of the dangers in the world, real or perceived and to act accordingly. When your mind starts to talk, criticize and judge, remember that this reflects a basic urge to protect yourself. You may then be more willing to accept what is being said and not personalize it.

# Practice

Like mindfulness, the techniques listed here take practice and development.

1. When your mind starts to talk to you about a situation ask, *"Is this true? Is there another way to look at this situation?"*
2. When you become aware of your inner voice, write down what it's saying on the left side of a sheet of paper, which you've divided vertically into three columns. In the first column, briefly note what your inner voice is saying. Put *"Is this true?"* at the top of the next column. At the top of the third write, *"Is there another way to look at it?"* Next, fill in the columns beside each phrase that your inner voice has to say. Sometimes it just helps slow your thoughts down to see them on paper. When you see what your inner voice is saying in writing, you can often see that it's being extreme, reactionary and is trying to scare you with the worst possible outcome.
3. Practice equanimity today with a stressful situation you may have recently encountered, even if it was a minor one. Ask yourself these questions: *"Can I change what has already happened in the past?" "Does worrying help the situation in any way?" "What can I do, at this point in time, to best deal with the situation?" and "What needs to be done?"*

# Summary

- Your inner voice comments on sensations and events from a perspective that is often exaggerated, unbalanced and catastrophizing (i.e., predicting the worst thing that can happen, often to a ridiculous extent).
- When you become aware of your inner commentary, ask yourself, *"Is this true?"* and *"Is there another way to look at this situation?"*

- Other techniques for de-stressing during a crisis include, focusing on another thought, focusing on the dominant word in the thought, allowing your inner voice to say what it has to say and using the question *"What's next?"* to interrupt your thoughts.
- Look for the intent behind your behaviour and be compassionate with yourself. Nobody's perfect.
- Feed the fire, in order to see the over-exaggerated nature of your self-criticisms.
- The process of examining whether your story about a situation is true or not and trying to look at the situation from another perspective is called *Reframing*.
- *Equanimity* is accepting events for what they are.
- You can't change what has already happened so focus on what you can do from now on. Recognize that you have made the best decision that you could have made for who you were at that point in time.

# 15

## Where Does the "I" Come From?

### When do you think of yourself as "I" and when do you just "B"?

IT MAY SURPRISE YOU TO KNOW that there isn't a conscious "I" that is operating all of the time. In fact, the sense of you as being an "I", a discrete entity or an individual, is constantly going through a process of creation and extinction. The "I" is not a solid permanent identity, but a fabricated, temporary, mental creation. Most of the time, your sense of your own identity as a unique, persisting, and separate being, is just not foremost in your mind or even required for that matter.

You're likely often present to what you experience without a sense of yourself as the inner "I" behind it. You hear the sounds of birds or cars, eat food, smell flowers, see the sun, go to the bathroom, walk, run, or drive with no conscious sense of an "I" who is doing these activities. You're on automatic pilot, navigating your way through the day. At those times you're just *the process of doing something without a sense of an "I" who is doing the act.* You don't need to be self-aware or engage in a self-assessment during these activities commonly, so you don't have a tendency to think, "I am driving" or "I am walking," as you privately go about routine tasks.

If you mindfully bring your awareness to the times when there is no "I" concept foremost in your mind, but rather just the process of *doing* something, you'll see that the essential "you" naturally operates from a place of peace and equanimity. By continuing to bring your attention to this place, you'll start to become familiar with this feeling. You'll quickly come to recognize that, for much of the day, your sense of self, or

separate identity is just not needed. You can and do function quite nicely without it most of the time.

## How is the concept of "I" created? Is there an "I" behind the seeing or is it just the eye?

It's interesting to see how the "I" is created in response to certain circumstances coming together. For example, if you forget to pay a bill, your mind starts to criticize you for your thoughtless action:

*The bill wasn't paid. This is terrible. I am bad!*

If you break this criticism down, it's interesting to view the chain of events that occurs. The initial event is the realization that a bill was not paid. An automatic and previously conditioned pattern in your mind then takes over. Not paying the bill on time is viewed as bad and unacceptable. A value judgment is placed on whatever you do by measuring it against your inner belief system, which in this circumstance states that it's important to always pay bills on time. This belief system came mostly from the values of your parents and caregivers. You adopted these values as a child to help guide your behaviour so that you would continue to be cared for and would not get into trouble. As a child you were very vulnerable and fundamentally feared abandonment or being overwhelmed.

The inner critic, triggered by a violation of your belief system, quickly takes control to go from *"this is bad"* to *"I am bad."* The "I" is intimately identified with your belief system. The inner voice, in effect, creates the concept of "I" as needed. It determines that the action was bad and generalizes, with the creation of the identity "I" that *"I am bad."* The "I" is the inner child, who now feels threatened because the action of not paying a bill is viewed as wrong.

The "I" is created when there is a perceived threat to the integrity of your internalized belief system. It reflects how you think you should behave in the world to maintain a feeling of being loved and accepted. The inner child feels threatened and those fears become expressed in your inner voice. *The inner child places itself in the situation of not having paid the bill and reacts to it.* In other words, if you're using the word "I," as part of a conversation that's taking place in your mind, watch out! A pattern of response from your early childhood has likely been triggered and you should be very wary about what it has to say!

*The "I" is the inner child who believes it has not acted in a manner that follows its belief system in order to maintain things in a safe fashion.*

The system needs to act defensively and the internal criticism reflects a child's attempt to guide his or her behaviour in the right way. The harsh and critical words of your own inner voice may even reflect things that were said to you as a child by your caregivers in previous situations.

# How Understanding the "I" Creation Helps You Deal With Stress

It's important for you to understand the relationship between the judgment of your action by your belief system and the subsequent personalization and creation of the "I". In understanding that not paying the bill is perceived as bad and that that action has triggered the creation of the "I", it allows you to more easily separate the action from the commentary.

Not paying your bill doesn't change your identity into that of a bad person! Your actions may be viewed as wrong according to your belief system but that doesn't make you a bad human being. All of this evaluating and judging occurs spontaneously and automatically, again reflecting the fact that much of your mental functioning is beyond your conscious control.

Ultimately, it's this referencing of how an event compares with your established patterns of belief that then creates the "self." Your sense of "I" keeps getting created and recreated in situations where there is a perceived challenge to your internal belief system, as a consequence of an external or internal sensation or event.

*So how does this help you deal with stress?* Bring your attention to the times that the "I" is created. *What are the circumstances that lead to the formation of the "I" for you personally?* By paying attention to what tends to happen just before you notice an internal conversation where you're using the word "I" a lot, you can identify the patterns that lead to "I" formation.

When you hear your inner voice using the word "I", (or for some people "you" in reference to themselves, e.g., "You shouldn't have done that!" "You're an idiot!" etc.), it's a big red flag that should warn you to examine the content of your own internal conversations extra-carefully. They're probably coming to you straight from your inner child and you know so much more now than you did when you were four! This should give you some perspective and allow you to calm down a bit, be less critical and judgmental and therefore reduce your stress.

You can now extend mindfulness to the whole process. A *sensation* (or if you prefer, think of it as a perception, stimulus, experience, or event) leads to a *story* about the sensation based on your belief system, which recruits your inner child, who then defines the *self*. For example, the *sensation* is not paying the bill. The *story* is that this is a problem and wrong. The *self* is created as expressed by the inner voice's statement, "I am bad."

Again, if you can just let yourself be aware of the whole mental process, then you'll be less likely to get carried away by the critical and negative comments in your stories during times of stress. This is the part of the process called *separation*. Instead you'll be more likely to be able to step back and say, *"Wait a second, you're the inner child my doctor warned me about!"* Separation does not mean walling yourself off from what's happening. It implies not taking ownership and not identifying with what has arisen.

# Mindfulness and the Stepping Back of Separation

(SENSATION → STORY → SELF → SEPARATION)

What's interesting is that the ultimate pain that produces your stress and your suffering doesn't come from the creation of the "I" but from *identifying with the created "I"*. You believe your story to be one hundred percent real and true, even though most of it was created as a coping mechanism when you could scarcely walk.

With time and experience, you know that stories change and are not permanent. So you know that your own story can't be the whole truth and nothing but the truth, but when you first hear it, it sure feels like the truth. You feel bad that you didn't pay the bill and you chastise yourself. If you let yourself get caught up in your own story and the belief that there is the "I" that is fundamentally bad, good, angry, sad, etc., your feeling of stress is bound to hang around. However, you can transcend the stress by bringing mindfulness into the moment.

Be present to what arises from a position of separation, as the witness or observer of the story and its process, without identification or attachment. The stress will start to dissipate. This isn't to say that you don't need to pay your bills, or that there are no consequences to your actions. A little stress can be an excellent motivator, but when your stories start to suck the life out of you and you really start suffering, it's good to know how your mind really works so that you can put a stop to it.

Your identification with your thoughts, emotions and physical sensations determines your own suffering. *The creation of the story and the self is not the problem.* If you understand that sensations, stories and even the self (that pops up as a star in your own melodrama), are all just mental states and conditioned patterns of reaction, then you can use all that you've learned about mindfulness to experience them without the pain of ownership.

The next time you catch your inner voice with something critical to say, see if you can clearly pinpoint what it's trying to tell you about who you are as a person. Pick out the key word or descriptor that it's using. If it's saying, "I am a bad person," for example, ask yourself:

*Am I truly a bad person or is this just a mental state?*

Also explore:

*Does the belief that I am bad realistically define who I am?*

In asking these questions, you will start to stand back a bit and give yourself some vital perspective. The union of Eastern mindfulness and the Western-based inquiry into the processes of the mind is a powerful one-two punch to your habitual stress responses.

As you have discovered, anxiety and stress come from the fact that everything you experience is examined to determine how it impacts your created sense of self or "I". You might feel hurt that someone didn't call you, that he or she ignored you, yelled at you, didn't include you, couldn't read your mind to know exactly what you wanted, etc. You'll find that it's very calming to just consider whatever is happening as a straightforward event, without having to self-reference it.

Try this experiment. Describe a stressful event in your life without using the word "I". For example, Larry bought his suit and his mind started to criticize him and say, "How *could I have bought such an expensive suit? I am terrible with money.*" Larry could reframe this and instead say to himself, "*A suit was bought. Fear and anger are present.*"

Here's another example. Mika made a mistake at work and a co-worker started to get upset with her. Normally Mika would have said, "*How could I have done this? I really made a bad mistake. I am so stupid!!*" Mika could take the "I" out of these sentences and say them to herself in a new way, for instance, "*The report was not ready. John is angry.*"

Pick something that's bothering you in your life right now and restate the problem as pure fact only. It can be tricky to let go of the "I" who is feeling hurt, but try to think about only the simple facts of a stressful situation. Again in Mika's case, a friend of hers was supposed to call her but didn't. Mika usually would have gotten very upset and would have said to herself, *"Why didn't Mary call me? What did I do? I don't like her!"* Instead, Mika could say, *"Mary did not call. Anger is present."*

Rather than getting caught up in the sense of the self having been wronged, hurt and not treated properly, try to see the event as it is, without the self-referencing. Give yourself the opportunity to look at what's happening objectively, without the emotional torment. You can then deal more effectively with the issue and will have a much better shot at solving the problem. The only true measure of your experience is whether it's ethically right, compassionate and wise.

## Practice

See if you can now try to bring your mindfulness practice to the process of

SENSATION → STORY → SELF → SEPARATION

1. Bring your awareness to situations when there is no "I" present. When you catch yourself doing something mundane or routine and are relaxed, drop in on your mind and see what it's doing.
2. Bring your awareness to situations when there is an "I" present. Ask yourself, *"What were the circumstances that led to the "I" formation?"* See if you can track it backward. Compare this state to what you experienced when you weren't thinking any "I"-related thoughts.
3. Pay attention to how your mind relates to the stories and the "I" that is created in response to a stress-inducing situation, action, event or sensation. Does the mind identify with, or separate from, the event?
4. Ask the question, *"Does the belief that there is an "I" that is bad (or whatever judgment is present for you at that moment) define my essence?"* As a human being you're a complex, dynamic,

unique individual. There is no one word that truly defines everything that you are.

## Summary

- You often go about your routine tasks without an "I" being present. You begin to use the word "I" in an inner commentary in response to a sensation or stimulus that causes you stress.
- The initiating sensation (action, stimulus, event, experience or perception) triggers an internal story to develop, which causes the need for the creation of a sense of self. A mental dialogue that includes the phrase "I" and is typically highly judgmental reveals this sense of self.
- The "I" is the inner child that has not acted in a manner that is perceived to be in-line with your internalized belief system. This system is a survival mechanism that was first established in your childhood.
- The inner child judges the sensation (action, stimulus, event, experience or perception) against its belief system and produces an inner commentary that includes wholesale value judgments such as, "I am a bad person."
- Stress and pain come from your personalization or identification with the story and your belief that the judgments of the inner voice are true.
- Bringing mindfulness to the chain of events from *sensation* to *story* to *self* will lead to a sense of *separation* from the entire process.
- With *separation* you have an opportunity to gain perspective and to understand that the inner voice is not speaking the ultimate truth, but is only a pattern that has persisted from your childhood.
- Mindfulness and *separation* will result in a reduction of your *stress* levels.

# 16

## Inner Child

## The Captain of Your Mind: Your Inner Voice

**A**S YOU'VE LEARNED THROUGHOUT THIS BOOK, each of us has his/her own personal *inner voice*, which is always commenting on, evaluating and criticizing what's going on in each of our lives. Consider for a moment whether or not your inner voice is usually saying nice or negative things. Think about whether you consciously determine what the voice is going to say next or not and for that matter, would you ever say the type of things your inner voice sometimes says to you, to another person?

The voice pops up in response to an external or internal sensation (experience, event, action, stimulus... you get the idea), comments on what has happened and directs the action to be taken next. The voice seems to be the controller of your mind but is it really? In the last chapter you learned that this voice is actually a pattern of response that you learned in childhood and is known as the *inner child*. It would be very helpful to have an understanding of the nature of this little captain of your mind.

The following is an example of a conversation (i.e., dialogue) with the inner voice. I think you'll find that eavesdropping on someone else's inner voice will help to illustrate the nature of the voice itself.

Larry was driving to work and he was becoming more and more agitated. The traffic was busy and he began to think that he was going to be late for work. He started to become increasingly anxious about this. His inner voice started to become stronger and it sounded something like this:

*I'm going to be late. Why do people have to drive so slowly? I will never get to work on time. I'm always late. Why did I leave home so late? Why did I take this road to get to work? How could I have made such a mistake? The boss is sure going to hate this. This is terrible!*

Seem a bit familiar?

Larry asked himself:
*Why is this so terrible?*
His inner voice said:
*If I keep doing this, my boss will fire me for sure. My goodness, if I was fired what would I do? I have a big mortgage. I could never keep that up without a job. I can't be late for work. I have to be on time. It's really important to be on time. It's important to do a good job.*
He asked the voice:
*Why is it so important to do a good job?*
Now the inner voice had really hit its stride:
*I have to do a good job. If I don't do a good job, that would be terrible! Oh no, I can't do a bad job. It has to be right.*
Larry asked the voice:
*Why does it have to be right?*
The voice answered:
*Oh no, it would be terrible. This is scary. I always have to do everything right. Everything has to be perfect. Everything has to be done the right way. If I do everything the right way I will be OK. I won't feel so frightened. I can't do it badly or I would be a failure. I am such a failure.*
Larry asked:
*Why are you such a failure?*
His inner voice had plenty to say about that! It had years and years of practice:
*I am always making a mistake. I can never get it perfect. I am so bad at whatever I do.*
Larry pursued the conversation with:
*Why are you so bad?*

His inner voice responded:

*Mom told me I was bad. Mom would always get so angry with me when I did something wrong. I always had to get everything right. I hated when she got angry with me. It scared me.*

Accompanying the dialogue, Larry also began to notice that he was starting to sweat, his pulse was becoming faster, his breathing shallower, he was shaking his head back and forth and he felt a familiar tightness in his abdomen.

Sometimes, there's no answer as to why, whatever it is, seems so terrible, but there can just be the feeling of unspoken fear, desperation, sadness, loneliness and hopelessness.

Larry was visibly upset and had reported that his Crohn's disease was really acting up and making him even more miserable. His boss hadn't come in that day, it turns out and Larry was only a few minutes late as a result of the traffic, but the inner voice kept at him for most of the day. By the time he came in to see me it had taken its toll.

This dialogue that Larry had with his inner voice illustrates that the voice was his inner child. The inner voice serves a very important function. It may seem harsh, critical and uncaring; on the contrary, *your inner voice is the child's protector*. It once guided your behaviour so that you acted in a way so as not to cause potential abandonment, and to protect yourself from feeling overwhelmed by your care takers.

The inner voice is not to be rejected or denied. It's still just trying to do its job and protect you. In fact, it should be embraced, as it reflects a true connection with the child you once were and his or her attempts to survive in this world. Try to think of it with some measure of love and compassion. It's a connection to your past and a window into how you functioned at that time, which is still influencing your present behaviour. It's an integral part of who you are and what drives your behaviour.

# Core Wounding and Your Body's Stress Response

When you experience an event as an adult, it's unconsciously examined by your internalized belief system. Your response is then directed by your need to stay within the parameters of this system. The upshot of this is that you're often being controlled by your inner four-year-old child's need for love, security, and acceptance.

Every child has experienced some 'core wounding.' Core wounding refers to experiences in your childhood, which were very emotionally powerful and may have related to loss, rejection, humiliation, betrayal and/or a sense of having been overwhelmed. As a child, you adopted various techniques to cope with these experiences. The legacy of these coping techniques may be that you have a set of behavioural tendencies that fit the common stereotypes of the perfectionist, the caregiver, the clown, or the renegade.

You originally developed these tendencies in response to emotional childhood events. As a child you responded to these events in a manner that made you feel less threatened and more comfortable, safe and accepted. As an adult your actions are still based on the same patterns that you developed as a child.

The inner voice actually brings you back to your childhood and how you experienced life at that time. The inner voice is really a child's response to events that are occurring now and how that child feels it measures up to its internalized parental values under the circumstances. Your belief system doesn't change very easily, especially if it seems to still be working for you. The belief system that you have in place now, that gives rise to the inner voice, was most likely first established in your childhood and has persisted into adulthood unchanged because it worked. At that early time in your life, it helped you cope. You're still alive. It helped you survive.

The inner child, however, does not differentiate between past and present. Everything that occurs now is interpreted from a point, which is fixed in the past when the belief was first developed. In most cases, this was when you were very young. So even though an event is occurring now and you have much more, knowledge, wisdom and experience that could help you cope, you're still habitually relying on the coping mechanisms that worked for the child you once were. That inner child is still reacting to current events with the emotional, psychological and physical responses of your past. Your inner child is still a child.

A belief-system pattern that arose out of a core-wounding childhood experience produces physical sensations when triggered. This is in response to the fear and anxiety you felt at the time of the original experience. You know these sensations as your own personal stress-response. You have a characteristic way of physically responding to your emotions that is entirely unique to you. This could be headaches, neck tension, shoulder pain, chest or abdominal pain, diarrhea, nausea, constipation or muscle spasms.

When you experience a physical reaction to something stressful, you're actually feeling the original physical memory pattern from your childhood, in response to a threatening episode from your past. Accompanying this is the general physiological response to stress, which includes rapid heartbeat, breath-holding, sweating, sleep disorders and fatigue.

Your response to events occurs on *two levels*. In Larry's inner-voice dialogue, there was the obvious surface fear of being late for work and the potential consequences that being late might cause for him as an adult. However, the true fundamental fear, resided in his inner child's response to this event. The most significant point here is that you have to dive deeper to truly understand what's motivating your behaviour.

For Larry, what actually was underlying his fear of being late for work was an earlier fear of not being good enough. His parents were very demanding and critical and nothing that Larry did was "good enough." This fear lead to a sense of perfectionism for Larry and he tried to be perfect in whatever he was doing in order to prevent any critical reactions. By being 'perfect' and controlling himself and his surroundings as best he could, Larry was able to minimize being yelled at or punished back when he was a child. The possibility of arriving late for work triggered Larry's fear surrounding childhood events that occurred relating to the completion of a task in a perfect way.

Review Larry's dialogue. You can see that the thoughts and actions he expresses, in his internal conversation, reflect learned behaviour from his childhood. You yourself, are also not operating entirely from an adult perspective, but carry your own inner child. If you can come to understand your own core-wounding experiences through a mindful dialogue with your inner child, you can see how these experiences and their aftereffects are manifested in all of your stress responses.

A common roadblock to meaningful change is that you probably believe that you're making conscious adult choices about how to act in this world. However, to a large extent, your behaviour is controlled by unrecognized, conditioned, habitual, childhood coping-strategies. You're not truly present to the events in your life, but to your inner child's interpretation of how the event fits with your internalized, parental belief system.

You judge everything you experience in order to position yourself in relation to the world so as to ultimately feel loved and safe. Your internalized parent (i.e., belief system) as voiced by your inner child, is constantly evaluating everything that you do. Did you make the right purchase? The right decision? Are you too fat or thin? Are you successful enough? The evaluation never ends.

Talking with your inner voice is a wonderful way to understand what's truly driving your "adult" behaviour. You have the ability to connect with your inner child through dialogues with that inner voice. Engaging in the dialogues will allow you to discover the true motives underlying how you operate in this world.

The inner child's belief system is the origin of the automatic responses and stories that you tell yourself about internal and external sensations, perceptions, experiences and events. Is this voice the one you want to be in control of your life? With additional insight, you can bring empathy, support and love to the process of trying to change. You can thereby diminish the power that your inner child has over your present day-to-day experiences. This will change how you respond to stress. It will give you more control, more perspective and that elusive peace of mind that we all dream about.

# Practice

1. The next time you become aware of an inner voice or conversation with yourself that's going something like, *"Oh I shouldn't have done that…"* look for clues that it's really a child talking. The voice will probably be using phrases such as, *"I'm in trouble. I'm so bad. You've done it now!"* etc. that are typical of childhood.

2. When you become aware of your inner child, extend compassion and understanding to the child you once were and use the occasion as an opportunity to explore why you think and act the way you do.

# Summary

- You have an *inner voice* that's always commenting to you during times of stress and directing the action to be taken next.
- This voice is a pattern of response that it helps to think of as your *inner child.*
- The events in your life are filtered and interpreted by your inner child to determine how they fit with your internalized, parental, belief system and both you and the events are judged accordingly.
- Every child has experienced *core wounding.* This refers to childhood events, which were very emotionally traumatic and may have related to loss, rejection, abandonment, humiliation, betrayal and/or a sense of having been overwhelmed.
- As a child you responded to core-wounding events in a manner that made you feel less threatened and more comfortable, safe and accepted.
- As an adult your actions are still based on the same patterns that you developed as a child.
- Your behaviour is controlled by these unconscious, habitual, childhood coping strategies (your inner child).

- By talking (i.e., having a dialogue) with your inner child, you can bring insight, empathy, support and love to the process of lessening the power that your childhood coping mechanisms have on your adult behaviour. This will help to reduce your stress levels.

# 17
## Dialogue:
## A Friendly Chat with Your Inner Child

## Your Inner child's Perspective

**A**RE YOU EVER AWARE OF AN INNER VOICE? If you were to develop mindfulness in relation to your own thoughts, you would discover that you have an inner voice that is *always* talking to you, usually criticizing, comparing and judging everything that arises internally and externally. You're not crazy to admit this. We all have this voice!

In this chapter, you'll learn a helpful stress-reducing technique, which is how to talk to your inner voice. This technique is called an inner-child dialogue.

The purpose of the inner-child dialogue is to:

- discover the underlying *core belief system* of the inner child
- examine if the core belief system is true
- identify the inner child's feelings

This is an important progression that ultimately helps you to change the limiting and painful belief system of the inner child.

The inner-child dialogue is a useful technique for really understanding yourself and your stress, but if you're new to it, it's going to seem a little strange at first. Just go with it as best you can. You'll get better at it and have more and more of those "Ah ha!" moments that are really transformational. Remember, you can't continue to handle things the way you always have and expect a different result. It's time for a change!

Often when you bring mindfulness to your powerful thoughts, it's hard not to identify with them. The other advantage of the inner-child dialogue is that, through this technique, you can truly understand that your inner voice is your inner child just trying to be safe. This understanding makes it easier to allow your thoughts to pass through your mind without taking any ownership of their content. You'll learn to recognize that your thoughts are not who you are. They are just coping mechanisms from your past.

The inner voice is really your protector, the voice that recognizes when you have strayed from your created belief system. It tries to promote balance and protect you and directs your actions accordingly. You should view the voice as that of your beautiful inner child who is trying to help you. If you keep this in mind, it may be easier to bring a sense of *self-compassion* to any conversations that you have with your inner child.

A conversation with your inner voice can take place on many levels. There is the surface level on which you, as an adult, have numerous worries and concerns in response to stressful events. However, it's the underlying realm of the inner child that *truly* gives a stressful event its motivational drive.

Have you ever noticed that in some situations there's an emotional or psychological intensity that appears disproportionate to what's actually happening? This intensity, or energy, is coming from your inner child. This is why connecting with the inner child, and truly understanding the experience from the inner child's perspective, can be so useful. Understanding can lead to meaningful change and change means less stress.

## Talking to Yourself

You're directly and intimately feeling the emotions and physical sensations that the inner child is experiencing and so you can authentically understand and express support to the inner child. The initial process of dialoguing follows this sequence:

1. Mindfulness: Bring awareness to your inner voice
2. "My dear child...": Recognize that your inner voice isn't you
3. Engage: Start a conversation with yourself
4. Inquire: Time to ask some questions

## Mindfulness: Bring Awareness to Your Inner Voice

Initially, to start an inner-child dialogue, you'll want to bring mindfulness into play. When practicing mindfulness, you bring your attention to the present moment without trying to change it and are simply present to whatever is being experienced. You're bringing awareness to what's being said, and what's felt emotionally and physically.

When a more emotionally charged thought arises and you notice your inner voice commenting, create some space around that sensation. Don't react to the voice. Just observe it; notice what it's saying to you from a place of awareness, acceptance, non-judgment, non-attachment and compassion. Initially, *don't do anything.* Just witness what presents itself. What's it saying? What's it feeling?

It can be very difficult not to identify with what the inner voice is saying and you may want to even amplify, or add to, what you're hearing. The initial ability to let the voice say what it needs to say, for as long as it needs to say it, without interfering, is the first step. You need to give voice to your inner voice.

When you're upset, you probably feel like talking to a friend and sharing with him or her what it is that you're experiencing. The opportunity just to be heard is likely more helpful than necessarily having your friend offer a solution.

You naturally are your inner child's best friend. You can truly experience mentally, emotionally and physically what the inner child is experiencing first hand, without having to guess at what's happening. In many situations, just listening and allowing the mind to speak will bring a stressful moment to a close without needing to do anything further. The child has normally felt neglected, marginalized and unimportant and finally there's some recognition.

It's essential that you really feel what the child is experiencing. This starts with really listening to the child, without interrupting, as it talks to you. Be completely open to feeling the emotional state of the child mentally and physically. Actively bring your attention to feeling the mental trauma and anxiety conveyed by your inner child, as well as any accompanying physical sensations, such as rapid or shallow breathing, racing heart rate, twisting sensations in the abdomen, shaking of the head or body, etc.

Immerse yourself in the experience in order to make meaningful change. Sitting in the fire of the emotional trauma of the child, and not running from it or avoiding it, will allow a transformation to occur. By directly experiencing what the child is feeling, you will be able to really determine, and then express, what it is that the child needs.

### "My Dear Child...": Recognize that Your Inner Voice isn't You

One of the biggest problems many people experience when first starting a conversation with their own inner voices is that they instantly and strongly identify with their own voices to the point where they can't easily distance themselves from them in order to engage in a dialogue. When you first begin the inner-voice conversations, you will tend to view the inner voice as completely "who you are."

To support the process of mindfulness, begin your dialogue with *"My dear child..."* This will serve as a reminder, which brings you back to the reality, that the inner voice is your inner child. It helps to create some space, away from the intensity of the inner voice, by clarifying the fact that who you are is not the voice. The voice represents your belief system and was formed in your childhood. It isn't who you are now! Remember that it's the voice of your inner child and this will allow you to keep your distance and listen to the inner voice with a sense of compassion.

What happens typically is that when the inner child starts to talk to you about its anxieties and concerns, your present-day awareness identifies with what's being said and amplifies what's being expressed. You then become the inner child with all of its fears. You react to the initial thoughts and have additional reactive thoughts that in-turn create more tension. This prolongs the interaction. The listening and supportive adult is lost, taken over by the inner child.

To avoid this, be careful not to identify with your inner voice by saying to yourself, "It's just my mind." The "my" part of that thought can lead to exactly the personalization that you're trying to avoid.

Consciously bring mindfulness to what's being said. *Follow the words* and feel their energy as events unfold. Don't identify with the content. Just bring your attention to what's being said for as long as your mind says it. Let your mind focus on the task of just listening. This gives your mind a job to occupy itself so that it doesn't have the chance to react and get more emotionally and/or actively involved. By being the observer, you shift the perspective and create distance. Ask yourself, *"What's being said?"* as a way of helping you to develop a greater sense of yourself as an observer in your own mind.

### Engage: Start a Conversation with Yourself

So you've observed that your inner voice (the voice of your inner child) has something to say. It's used to being the one in charge and you don't usually challenge it, especially during times of stress when you function on autopilot and are very reactive rather than responsive. Now is the time to start dialoguing with that inner voice.

### Inquire: You're in the Driver's Seat, Ask the Questions

- Remind yourself, once again, of the fact that this is a conversation with your inner child by opening the inquiry with, *"My dear child..."*
- The questions you pose to your inner child should be in the form of an *open-ended* question. Open-ended questions are just questions that can't be answered with a straight 'yes' or 'no' response. For example, it's not *"Are you feeling sad?"* but *"How are you feeling?"*
- Start your questioning with *"Why?"* Don't ask questions such as, *"Are you upset? Is something making you afraid? Do you want something?"* which are all questions that could be answered with a simple, and not very helpful, 'yes' or 'no'.
- *Base the rest of the questions on your inner voice's last response.* If the inner voice said, *"This is terrible!"* ask, *"Why is this so terrible?"* If the inner voice said, *"I am in trouble,"* ask, *"Why*

*are you in trouble?"* Remember to try to keep the questions in the open-ended format mentioned above. You don't want to ask questions that can be answered with a simple 'yes' or 'no'. You can base your next question on the dominant word in your inner voice's response.

- Talk to the voice as if you're talking to another person, but you don't have to have this conversation out loud by any means!

- Trust that whatever pops up comes from your inner child.

- Don't be dismissive about what's said. This is just an exercise. You're trying to help yourself manage stress better. Be open to whatever conversation naturally arises.

- Don't try to give advice or support at first. You're just there, initially, to *listen.*

- Don't rush the conversation. Allow the inner child to fully express what it's feeling. Give it time.

- Your ultimate intention, in asking these questions, is to try to discover the core belief system that underlies the pattern of behavior that has been triggered and is now being voiced by your inner child. The original experience that caused this belief system and behavior pattern to enter your repertoire was probably a core-wounding experience. Remember that core-wounding experiences most likely involved an event perceived by the inner child to have been emotionally traumatic and were likely related to loss, rejection, humiliation, abandonment, betrayal and/or a sense of having been overwhelmed.

- At times, the inner voice can't answer, completely, what it is that it's afraid of, but there will be a physical expression of fear in the body that you can clearly sense. There can also be the physical memory of how the inner child felt at that original time when this response pattern was first used in your childhood. This physical memory may produce hand wringing, head turning or bobbing, shallow breathing or holding of the breath, and/or tightness in the chest or abdomen. Bring awareness to the associated physical component as a way of fully becoming aware of what the inner child is experiencing in the moment.

You can further cultivate your inner-child connection by imagining that you're talking to yourself as a young child who is suffering. Reflect on a memory of a painful situation when you were a child. Hold that image in your mind when you're talking to the inner child. If that proves difficult to imagine, hold an image in your mind of a young child you deeply care for e.g., a niece, nephew or child of a friend, as you conduct your inner-child dialogues. You can also imagine holding the child in your arms when you talk to him/her. This visual image can be a powerful way to convey acceptance and love.

## How Does the Child's Belief System Influence Your Actions as an Adult?

Inner-child dialogue helps to bring your belief system into the light of day. It helps you to better understand where your emotional and physical reactions, as well as your sense of stress, may be coming from. Let's take a look at a situation, that my patient Larry experienced, as an example of an inner-child dialogue that revealed an important part of Larry's belief system.

Larry was out shopping for a new suit. He found one that was expensive but he decided to buy it. Shortly after that, his mind started to say:

*How could you have bought this suit? It's so expensive! What a mistake! This is terrible!*

Larry started an inner-child dialogue:

*My dear child, why is this a mistake?*

His inner voice said:

*The suit was way too expensive! This was wrong!*

Larry asked:

*Why was this wrong?*

The voice said:

*I can't spend money like this. It's not right. I have to save my money.*

Larry asked:

*Why do you have to save money?*

The voice answered:

*I can't spend all my money. That would not be safe.*

Larry asked:

*Why would that not be safe?*

The voice answered:

*Because I would get in trouble. Mom didn't like to spend money and that was the way it was. I always did what mom said!*

Larry asked:

*Why did you always do what your mom said?*

The voice responded:

*I always did what mom said. I would feel very frightened if I didn't.*

Larry asked:

*Why would you feel frightened?*

The voice said:

*Mom would get very angry. She would be very quiet and look at me in a mean way. That was so scary.*

Larry asked:

*Why was that so scary?*

The voice answered:

*I didn't like it when mom got angry with me. It made me feel that I was bad, that I had done something wrong. I was scared that something bad would happen to me if I didn't do what mom said. I always had to do whatever mom said. I needed to be perfect. I was scared that mom wouldn't love me anymore. I was scared that I would be all alone.*

In the above inner-child dialogue, what became apparent was that the child viewed buying the suit as a terrible event. The child was initially talking about its belief that it's bad to spend a lot of money. However, the underlying belief was that to spend a lot of money went against what his mother believed in. In not following his mother's beliefs, the inner child felt scared and threatened. Larry's inner child felt unloved and feared abandonment by his mother as a result.

What becomes apparent with inner-child dialogue is that the common themes of feeling unsafe, unlovable and not worthy ultimately drive our behaviors. The apparent fear of spending too much money was not the real reason for Larry's emotional reaction.

Larry's conversation with his inner child really took place on two levels. The first thing that Larry's inner voice had to say was that there was an adult concern that Larry had spent too much money on the suit and that this was not good financial management. However, the real issue was that his inner child's belief system said that it's actually dangerous to spend money.

Larry's parents, like mine, were immigrants and they didn't have a lot of money when they came to their new country. The lesson Larry learned, when he was growing up, was that it was important to save and not spend. It made no difference that Larry was an adult and could make an adult decision about whether or not he could afford the suit. In Larry's mind he had gone against his belief system about money, a belief system established before he was four years old.

*A common theme, that underlies much of the inner child's belief system, as well as the actions that are a result of this system, is the need to control the environment, in order to feel safe and loved by caregivers.*

You have discovered that Larry's inner child needed to feel safe by being "perfect" and this controlled his adult behavior. His mother controlled his actions and he felt overwhelmed. However, if he did something wrong, his mother withdrew and he felt abandoned. If Larry controlled his environment, as best he could, by trying to be "perfect", he could avoid the fear of going against the belief system, as communicated to him by his mother, and its potentially disastrous childhood consequences. Larry's need to be perfect influenced all of his adult actions.

Your own inner child also reacts to your experiences by referencing them to your established belief system. This process of reacting to what's being experienced is constantly and repetitively being played out.

Your inner child will use similar words to express a fearful reaction to wildly different experiences if they trigger the same childhood memories. These words will be based on a core-wounding experience. What this means is that you can look for certain words and phrases, when you're stressed, as clues to tell you whether or not your inner child is responsible for your stress-reaction. These inner comments often start with "I am _____".

Here are some examples of typical beliefs that come from a person's inner child. See if you recognize any of these beliefs in yourself. Look for similar statements when you are having an inner-child dialogue. Try to find what some of your unrealistic core beliefs might be in order to begin to change them and reduce your stress levels.

- I need to be perfect to be loved.
- I need to be in control of everything.
- I should not show my emotions.
- I am responsible for other people's feelings.
- My caregivers' needs are more important than my own.
- I need to take care of other people to be loved.
- I need to make other people happy to be loved.
- I am not loveable.
- I am not safe.
- I am not worthy.
- I am flawed.
- I always make mistakes.
- I am bad.
- I deserve to be treated poorly.
- I need to work hard at the expense of everything else.
- I should spend my money.
- I should save my money.
- I need to make a lot of money to feel safe.
- I should have no needs.
- I should not ask for anything.
- I need other people to take care of me.

Larry used a lot of "Why?" questions to really get to the root of his inner child's concerns. Sometimes, in an inner-child dialogue, you'll reach a point with these "Why?" questions where your inner child can't really answer why it's feeling the way it is. However, the child is obviously scared, sad, angry etc. You might feel associated physical symptoms such as your heart racing, increased sweating, abdominal squeezing, clenching of the jaw or other physical expressions of stress that are unique to you personally. At this point, other questions are necessary to further explore the inner child's belief system. One important question to ask your inner child is, "*What are you feeling?*"

## *What is the Feeling?*

It's important to understand and acknowledge what the inner child is feeling in the moment. Larry targeted his inner child's feelings directly.

> Larry asked:
> *What are you feeling?*
> The voice answered:
> *This is pretty scary!*

Sometimes it works just to reflect back, or repeat, what you think your inner child is feeling, for example:

> Larry stated:
> *It sounds like you're feeling scared.*

You may have all kinds of different feelings in response to an external or internal event. However, there is a difference between your *expressed feeling* and the underlying *core feeling*.

Using the inner-child dialogue you'll discover that your inner child's belief system is what's innately responsible for your feelings. You may express anger but actually be feeling fear. Often, this is a version of a fear of abandonment or of being overwhelmed that you had as a child as you struggled to behave in a way that made you feel safe and loved by your parents. In response to a situation, your inner child reacts the way it does in order to protect you.

Diving deeper beneath the expressed feeling to identify the core feeling will allow you to understand what's really happening in any particular situation. You can then be more fully present when you are experiencing stress. You will be able to approach situations with a greater sense of compassion. You will be able to act instead of just reacting. Being able to identify the *expressed feeling* and the underlying *core feeling* provides additional clarity and freedom.

## Helping Your Inner Child Understand the Meaning of Its Own Belief System

Remember that you are using the technique of inner-child dialoguing to get to the heart of your stress-reactions. Your inner child is frequently in a panic about something you have done or something that has happened to you. It communicates with you as though everything that happens is a big catastrophe, as if something is the worst, most horrible thing that could have happened. It's very tempting to accept the inner child's panic as legitimate but if you want to de-stress, you'll have to dig deeper. In the next part of the process, you'll continue the inner-child dialogue and explore the specifics of the inner child's understanding of its own belief system.

When the inner child makes a comment such as how terrible or scary something is, you can use this as an opportunity to ask the inner child, for the first time, to really begin to explain, or examine, what it understands about its own belief system.

Ask your inner child a version of, "*What does terrible/horrible/bad mean?*"

### What Does Terrible/Horrible/Bad Mean?

In Larry's inner-child dialogues, his inner voice was frequently fretting and saying, "This is terrible."

Larry asked:
*What makes this so terrible?*

His inner voice answered:

*Oh no this is really bad. I really made a mistake! Any mistake is terrible!*

Clearly, Larry's inner child has absolutely no leeway. It needs to be perfect in every way. Any mistake is viewed as terrible. Your own inner child may not be able to answer why something is so catastrophic until you examine the specifics of the inner child's beliefs in a given circumstance. So your next step is to ask, "*What is the specific belief?*"

### What is the Specific Belief?

If the child seems to hold a belief about money, for example, you'd begin to target your questions to explore that belief. If your inner child was commenting that it was unlovable, or that you should have done something, or shouldn't have done something, then you would directly question those beliefs. In Larry's case, the inner child seemed to be upset about spending money.

Larry asked:

*What does it mean to save money? How much can you spend on a suit? $100, $200, $500 dollars? How much do you need to save?*

The voice of his inner child answered:

*Um, I'm not so sure.*

Larry's inner child didn't know how to answer the question. This is quite common. Larry's inner child held the belief that it learned from his parents that it was not good to spend money and one should save money. However, since the inner child unconditionally takes on the general belief systems of its caregivers without the knowledge or insight to really understand what any of the beliefs really mean, it struggles to respond to direct questions.

It's quite interesting to ask the child specific questions about its belief system and see that system begin to collapse like a house of cards. Your own inner child probably does not know what its beliefs really mean. It borrowed the belief system of your parents or caregivers when you were very young because it had to, to feel safe and loved. As you start to question your own beliefs via inner-child dialogue, they won't have as much power to make you panic and worry.

### What Does it Mean to Be Safe, Lovable and Worthy?

A common inner-child belief is that the child needs to be perfect and accepted by its caregivers to feel safe, lovable and worthy. This can be the most difficult part of the belief system to examine. Any perceived act that doesn't follow what the caregivers want is viewed as dangerous to the child.

To examine your own inner child's beliefs ask the child directly.

Larry asked his inner child:

*What does it mean to you to be safe, lovable or worthy?*

The voice responded:

*I feel safe when I am not scared of what mom or dad will do if I don't do everything they want from me. When they are happy with me and what I do, I feel good and I'm happy too.*

You can see that feeling safe, loveable and worthy is dependent on the parents' approval of what the child has done. The child doesn't feel that it has any real value. Everything is conditional. Love can be taken away at any moment. Your inner child is constantly on the alert for threats to your belief system in its efforts to keep you safe, but does it really make sense that you have to be perfect and accepted by everyone in order to feel good about yourself?

# Exploring the Validity of the Belief System

The inner child holds beliefs that it feels to be true. You were powerless when you were growing up. The child you once were took what you experienced and drew conclusions. You saw what behaviors made you feel safe and what made you feel unsafe. That was your reality and you never questioned it. However, you now have the ability to bring your adult consciousness to the child's belief system. You now have the skills to examine whether that belief system is true or not and reflect this back to your inner child.

You can use the following questions to begin a targeted dialogue that will question whether beliefs that you have held for a lifetime are true, realistic and ultimately valuable to you or not. You will ask your inner child, "*Is it really that bad?*" "*Are you safe?*" and finally, "*Are you loveable and worthy?*"

### Is It Really that Bad?

To explore whether these core beliefs are true, you began by asking some targeted questions about what the beliefs were and what they meant. Now you will begin to question whether these beliefs are really true using your inner child's own choice of words. For example, when Larry's inner child was saying that buying the suit was "terrible", Larry asked, "*Is it terrible?*"

Larry didn't stop the questioning there. He also asked:

*Was anyone hurt? Did anyone die? Will you be bankrupt? Is this something that is extremely bad? Is this the worst thing to happen in the world?*

The voice answered:

*Well I guess not. Nothing really that bad happened.*

### Are You Safe?

The next question to ask your inner child, after addressing how bad the situation, action or occurrence actually is, is simply, "*Are you safe?*" If your dialogue has already revealed some of the origins of your belief system, then you can use that information as well, to make your questions more effective and specific.

Larry asked:

*Are you safe right now? I know you feel scared and not safe when mom becomes quiet and mean. What happens after she becomes quiet? What is the worst that can happen to you?*

Larry's inner voice said:

*She is quiet for a while and then she starts to talk again. I am ok when she doesn't talk. Nothing really bad happens.*

Larry asked his inner child:

*Is she here right now to punish you, not talk to you or be mean to you? Can anyone hurt you at this moment?*

The voice answered:

*I feel scared but you're right. I am ok. There's no one here to hurt me.*

### Are You Lovable and Worthy?

Examining the validity of the belief that the inner child is not safe, loveable or worthy is the most difficult process. The child has a very strong fear of abandonment. It doesn't feel that it has any value. The child only feels loved based on how well it's following the belief system of the caregiver in any given moment. Take a look at how Larry handled examining the truth behind his inner child's beliefs.

Larry asked:

*Are you loveable and worthy? I know that you believe that you have to be perfect to be loveable. Can anyone be perfect in this world? Is your mom always perfect? Are you only lovable if you're perfect?*

*Can anyone control every moment in life?*

*Because you bought the suit, this makes you totally unlovable and unworthy? Is your ability to be loved only based on what you do every moment?*

*How would you treat a scared child if he made a mistake?*

*Do you deserve to be punished if you're not perfect?*

*Did you intentionally act in a bad way?*

*In order to be loved you feel like you need to do whatever your mom demands. Is she always right, fair or kind?*

*Do you deserve to be heard as a child?*

*As a child you are small and powerless. Shouldn't your parents take care of you unconditionally?*

As the child sees that the beliefs it holds are not valid, not real, there can be some loosening of these strongly held beliefs. The child may be able to see, with more clarity, what's really happening in a stressful situation. This clarity will ultimately make you less reactive and less stressed, as you continue with the practice of inner-child dialoguing.

### Is It Fixable?

The child often operates from a place of powerlessness. It's dependent on caregivers and doesn't feel that it's capable of dealing with any real or perceived problems that may arise. However, the child still has a sense of justice and injustice, of what's right or wrong. The wisdom of the adult is also present at this point to help guide the child.

So far, you have begun an inner-child dialogue, most likely during a stressful time. You have listened to the child and have asked questions to try to discover some of the child's inner, core beliefs. You've also begun to connect how these beliefs are affecting your actions as an adult.

You've helped your inner child begin to understand the meaning behind some components of its belief system and you've uncovered some specific beliefs related to your current stressful situation, such as "spending money is bad". Finally, you've challenged this belief by asking the inner child, "Is the situation really that bad?" "Are you safe?" and "Are you loveable and worthy?"

Now you need to ask your inner child one final, all-important question which is, "Is this fixable and if so, what needs to be done?"

Larry asked his inner child:

*What needs to be done?*

*Is there a solution to this problem? Is it fixable?*

The voice of his inner child answered:

*Well, I bought the suit. I guess I can afford it and I can keep it.*

Of course, if Larry could not really afford the suit he could return it, sell it or find some way to make extra money to help pay for it. If the inner child can't offer a solution, that's perfectly ok. The adult part of who you are can respond and come up with some possibilities.

Remember, that choosing to do nothing, in a given situation, may also be a solution.

When you are focused on finding a possible solution to a problem or situation, your inner child can see that problems are not so overwhelming. There's always some kind of a solution to whatever happens even if it's not ideal. There's a way forward. The child is not powerless. However, this "fixing" must take place on two levels. There's the obvious, perceived problem, e.g., spending too much money, and then there's the more significant underlying issue of the inner child's distorted belief system.

## Inner-Child Dialogues in Action

I hope you will take some time to have a conversation with your inner child the next time you're stressed. My personal approach to inner-child dialogues, as well as the suggestions that I have given you for what questions to ask your inner child, will get you started. You are free to use whatever works for your particular situation. The underlying process remains the same in that, through inner-child dialogue, you are trying to identify the belief system, have the child clearly define what the belief system means and then examine the truth of it.

The core belief system really is the controlling force in your behavior and it's amazing how it impacts your day-to-day activities. Let's look at how Larry's core belief system influenced his life:

- When someone was driving too slowly in front of him, Larry became upset. His inner voice started to say, "Look at how that person is driving. This is terrible. He is so slow. He shouldn't be allowed to drive!" After Larry talked to his inner child, he realized that he was upset because the other person was not driving in a way that Larry felt was perfect.

  In his mind Larry had placed himself in the car that the other person was driving and became anxious because the other person was not driving the way that Larry felt was the right way to drive. This made Larry uncomfortable as it triggered a memory of his childhood experiences. Larry needed to be in control in order to feel safe.

- When Larry was bowling and one of the competitors scored low, Larry felt happy and superior. His inner voice said, "Look how that other person bowled. She is such a poor bowler. I am so much better than her!" Talking with his inner child once more, it became evident that Larry's sense of happiness came from the feeling that he was "perfect" and/or better than someone else. This also made him feel safer and less vulnerable.

- Larry got into an argument with a colleague and started to tremble inside. His inner voice said, *"How dare that person talk to me that way. This is horrible! He's so stupid and mean. I hate him!"* When he held a dialogue with his inner child later that day, it triggered the memory of the feeling he would experience when his mother was upset with him.

  His words "I hate him" were really a reflection of the words he used as a defenseless child who would silently say, "I hate you" to his domineering mother. On the surface level, Larry was upset with his colleague over the fact that he was yelling and not treating Larry respectfully. However, at a deeper more significant level, it brought up childhood memories of when his mother used to yell at him.

- When Larry forgot to call a friend back, or respond to an email in a timely fashion, or when he cheated on his diet, yelled at his kids, said something snippy to a colleague, forgot to exercise regularly, neglected to change his winter tires before the snow came, tripped in front of his friends, didn't eat enough fruits and vegetables, bought some expensive clothes or new sports equipment, missed the special sale on electronics, took time off for himself etc. etc. etc. his critical mind would kick in. His mind would comment on, criticize, compare and judge everything he did!

Mika also had a personal story that was the underpinning of all her thoughts and actions. She grew up in a family where her father was an alcoholic and could be verbally and physically abusive to the family. She didn't know, when she was coming home from school, whether her father was going to be nice or abusive. Any excessive display of emotion could trigger a reaction from her father.

Mika learned to be invisible and bottle up all of her emotions. When she would ask her mother why her father was being mean to her, her mother would say, *"Your father's not mean. He's just trying to be a good parent. If he's upset, you must have done something that was wrong. I don't know where you got the idea he was not being nice to you."* Mika learned from her mother that she could not trust her own feelings and viewpoints. She didn't receive any validation. She had to be invisible. She could not ask for anything for herself. She was also made to feel responsible for other people's feelings.

By the time I met Mika, she had a long history of abdominal pain, nausea and fatigue. This really reflected a physical expression of her emotional issues. As she continued to push her feelings down, they leaked out through her physical pores. Her body expressed what was going on in her mind.

Anytime she was in a situation where she, even remotely, perceived that someone was upset with her, she would feel anxious. It didn't have to be an extreme example. Even an innocent comment by someone could trigger an internal response.

One day when Mika was at work, she brought a file to her boss. The boss said to her, *"That's the wrong file. Could you bring me the right one?"* Instantly, Mika felt nauseated and experienced abdominal pain.

Let's look at Mika, in this situation, as another example of how an inner-child dialogue can be rewarding. You'll see how to put it all together using the process and questions that we've covered so far.

In response to her boss's request for a different file, Mika's inner voice became active. She noticed that she was repeating certain negative comments and questions to herself and this became her cue to initiate an inner-child dialogue to reduce her stress levels.

Mika's inner voice was saying:

*This is terrible. How could I have made such a mistake?*

Mika asked:

*Why is this terrible?*

The voice responded:

*Can't you see what I did? I didn't bring the right file. How could I have done this? I am always making a mess. I am hopeless.*

Mika asked:

*Why are you hopeless?*

The voice seemed upset:

*I never do anything right. I am always making a mistake. I hate you! I hate you!*

Mika asked:

*Who do you hate?*

The voice answered:

*I hate dad. He was always so mean to me. I couldn't do anything without him yelling or hitting me. I could never do anything right! I always had to be so careful. I had to be perfect.*

Mika asked:

*How did that make you feel?*

The voice responded:

*It made me feel so scared. I didn't know what to do. I never wanted to be home. I just wanted to hide away.*

Mika asked:

*It sounds like you were feeling both scared and very angry.*

The voice responded:

*Yes I was very angry! It felt so unfair! I hate him. I hate him!*

What came out in the dialogue was that the surface situation of not bringing the right papers to her boss, and the fear of not doing a good job and being fired, was not the real reason for Mika's intense stress-reaction. It was the childhood memory of her father's anger that the situation triggered that was the real source of her stress, fear and anger. This was a very valuable discovery for her that a quick dialogue brought to light. She was then able deal directly with the underlying motive for her behaviour.

Mika can use further internal dialogue to examine other areas, such as what her inner child understands about the meaning behind its belief system, what safe, loveable or worthy means to the child etc., just as with Larry's example. Mika has the opportunity to comfort her inner child and reassure it that her experience with her boss is not the same as what she endured with her father. She also has a chance to examine the validity of her belief system to reduce the likelihood of future over-reactions.

Mika's history of abuse is a very powerful example of the trauma the inner child may have experienced. It can be very difficult to shift the belief system in such a situation. However, an effective means of loosening the grip of this unconscious force is to examine whether the child's belief system is valid, reasonable, or true.

Here is another sample conversation to show you how inner-child dialogue can be developed to get at the root of a stress-reaction. To question the truth of the inner child's beliefs, Mika began with some questions regarding the feelings of the child in relation to love and self-worth.

Mika asked:

*It seems that to be loveable and worthy you have to do everything that your father wants. You can't make a mistake. If you do then there's a problem. Is there anyone you love and why do you love that person?*

The voice responded:

*I love my grandmother. She is so sweet and kind. She holds me, tells me that she loves me and gives me cookies.*

Mika asked:

*Does she love you even if you make a mistake?*

The voice answered:

*One time I broke a glass and grandma said it was ok, nothing to be upset about. I was so scared but it was all right.*

Mika commented:

*So it seems that you can be loved even if you're not perfect, even if you don't do everything that your dad wants.*

The voice seemed calmer as it said:

*Yes, that seems right.*

Mika continued:

*Are you a good person? What things do you do that are nice?*

The voice responded:

*I try really hard. I clean up my room and take the plates to the sink. I play with my baby brother. I am a good person.*

Mika continued trying to help the child examine its own beliefs:

*It seems that you are a good person whether you are perfect for your dad or not. Do you ever mean to be bad or hurt anyone?*

Her inner voice said:

*No! I never try and be mean or bad. I never want to hurt my brother, mother, father or my best friend.*

Mika reassured her inner child:

*If you don't intend to be mean or bad to anyone then no one can be angry at you for what you do.*

Mika continued:

*Is your father always right? Does he ever make a mistake?*

The voice answered:

*Well he got a ticket for speeding once and another time he yelled at me when there was dirt all over the carpet. It was the dog that brought in the dirt and not me.*

Mika summarized a key point and then continued:

*It seems that your father is not perfect. No one can be perfect. Why is it important that everything be controlled?*

The voice of her inner child answered:

*If I can make everything perfect then there will be nothing that I do that will upset my father. He won't get angry with me and I will feel safe.*

Mika asked:

*Can you control everything that's going to happen? What can you control? Do you know what's going to happen in the next moment?*

The voice paused before answering:

*Let me see. I can control what clothes I'll wear today. But no, I don't know what's going to happen next.*

Mika went on:

*You're right. No one knows what's going to happen in the next moment. If no one can know this, then how can you make everything perfect and controlled so that nothing will happen that will disturb your father? Just allow things to happen, because you can't do anything else.*

Mika then asked:

*Your father hit you when he felt that you made a mistake or spoke the wrong way. Did that seem fair? Do you deserve to be punished if you make a mistake? How would you treat a child if she made a mistake?*

Mika's inner child answered:

*No one deserves to be hit. That's wrong. That's not fair. I am a good person. I would tell the child that it's ok. She doesn't have to worry. I would play with her.*

When Mika dialogued with her inner child and examined what was happening, the child finally had an opportunity to say what it believed. There's a natural wisdom in the inner child that knows what's right and what's wrong, what's fair or unfair.

Mika asked:

*Can you ever ask for anything for yourself?*

The voice responded:

*Oh, no I can't ask for anything for myself. That would not be right.*

Mika asked:

*Why would that not be right?*

The inner voice answered:

*I would not want to make dad angry. What would happen if he didn't like what I said? I just need to make him happy. I just need to hide.*

Mika addressed the fear she heard in the voice directly:

*You sound very scared. Is your father here now? Can he hit you now?*

The voice pondered:

*Well I guess that's true. He isn't here right now. But it still feels scary.*

Mika responded:

*I know that it feels scary but you're safe right now. There's no one here to hurt you. I'm here and I'll keep you safe. If you need something don't you think that it's ok to ask? If one of your friends asked for part of your cookie would you share it with him? Do you think that it's ok for him to ask?*

The voice brightened:

*Sure I would share my cookie with my friends. It's ok for them to ask.*

Mika reasoned:

*It seems that you feel that it's ok for other people to ask for things. It only seems fair that you have the same opportunity. If what you are asking for is fair and not greedy then it's ok to ask.*

Mika continued:

*When your dad gets angry do you tell him to be angry? Do you choose whether he is going to be happy or sad or does he make that choice for himself?*

The inner voice responded:

*I never want my dad to be angry. I would only want him to be happy.*

Mika continued to offer her adult perspective:

*Only we can make ourselves happy or sad. You are not responsible for your dad's emotions. He makes that choice for himself.*

The above dialogues give you an example of the different questions you could ask to explore the *validity* of the inner child's belief system. The child has held on tightly to its beliefs without any critical questioning of them. For the first time, the child has the ability to examine the truth behind its beliefs.

As you continue to take the opportunity to challenge the beliefs of your own inner child, you will find that the way you react to potentially stressful situations will begin to change. Review the inner-child dialogues given here after you have given them a try for yourself. See if you can make use of any of the questions or lines of reasoning. Tailor your questions to your own history and beliefs and don't let your inner child squirm out from under some of the tougher questions. Keep it up. Keep trying. Change takes time. You can do it.

# Early Child-Parent Relationship

You'll also find it interesting and informative to explore how the inner child experienced its (your) childhood. When you understand what your childhood was like, this will give you further insight into the origins of some of the ways you learned to cope.

*What was the relationship between you, as a child, and your parents?* What went on as your inner child was growing up? How was the inner child treated? Once again, you can think about these questions from your grown, adult perspective but you can use the technique of inner-child dialogue to go even deeper.

> Larry asked himself:
>
> *How did you feel about your childhood?*
>
> His inner voice responded:
>
> *I was very angry. It was so unfair. No one really cared about what I wanted. No one listened to me. What I had to say wasn't important. So how could I be important? I always had to make Mom happy. I always had to be perfect. It was the only way to feel safe around Mom. If everything were under control, then Mom wouldn't be upset. I had to always be on guard. I felt so scared and angry whenever I thought that I had done something wrong.*

Your early parent-child relationship can be further explored with additional questions for the inner child such as:

- *What was it like to be a child?*
- *How did your parents treat you?*
- *Did you feel loved?*
- *Were you seen?*
- *Were you heard?*

> Larry asked these questions and his inner voice answered:
>
> *No one ever listened to me. Mom would always tell me what to do, what to wear and what to eat. It was always about what made her happy. She was always criticizing what I did. She never cared about*

*what I wanted. I could never make a decision that I wanted to make. If I made a mistake then Mom would be mean to me and not talk to me. It was frightening. I didn't want that to happen. I felt that everything had to be perfect to feel ok. If I made a mistake, I felt bad and scared.*

This dialogue revealed to Larry that his inner child never felt safe, loved or accepted. The child was overwhelmed by his mother and his coping strategies were based on this core wounding. Remember that these conversations can be very emotional for you and that you don't have to ask everything in one sitting. This is a process. Be kind to yourself.

## What Does the Child Need to Say to Its Caregivers?

Understanding what the child needs to say to its caregivers is also important. A caregiver may be a parent, an older sibling, another relative, a babysitter, or a teacher who was present at a core-wounding moment. Now you can take some time to explore what the inner child truly would like to say to its parents/caregivers.

The inner child has kept its true feelings secret for many years. It would have been far too intimidating, or threatening, for the child you once were to directly comment to a caregiver on how the child perceived the way in which he or she was being treated. The inner child can finally express how it feels in the safety of the inner dialogue. This, at long last, gives a voice to the child. The child is no longer invisible, unseen and unheard.

In expressing these feelings, the inner child can finally feel that it has value and meaning. What the child says is important and needs to be taken into consideration. This can start the process of healing the wounds caused by feeling marginalized and unacknowledged.

Larry asked his inner child:
*What would you like to say to your parents?*

The inner child answered:

*I am really angry. Why did I always have to be perfect? Why did I always have to do things your way? Why couldn't you allow me to make up my own mind? Why couldn't I have a say about what I wanted to do? Why did you always have to yell at me? Why did you always have to criticize me? I could never be right! Why didn't anybody ever listen to me? It was not fair. I didn't deserve to be treated like that. I AM a good person!*

## What Does the Child Need to Hear From its Parents?

A part of the child's healing comes from what it would like to hear from its parents. The child needs to hear that it's important and right. Even though the validation is imaginary, it can be very soothing.

Larry asked:

*What would you like to hear from your parents?*

Larry's inner voice responded:

*We're so sorry. We love you dearly. We didn't know that we were hurting you. We were just trying to do the best we could. However, we made mistakes in what we were doing and we apologize. You're a wonderful, delightful child and we're so sorry that we hurt you.*

## What Does the Inner Child Need?

After the child has expressed its feelings to its caregivers, it's time to discover what the inner child wanted or needed from them. You can ask this of the child in an open-ended and direct question, "*What do you need?*"

Larry asked his inner child:

*What do you need?*

His inner child replied:

*I need to feel loved, safe and accepted. I want to be seen and heard. I need you to listen to what I have to say without judging it. I don't want to be criticized about everything I do. I need to feel that I am OK without having to be perfect! I just want to have fun without worrying all the time. I want to feel that everything is ok. I don't want to feel afraid.*

You have a wonderful opportunity to directly experience, cognitively and emotionally, what the child is feeling in real time. You "walk in the shoes" of the inner child as the experiences of the inner child are alive within you at this moment. You have the unbelievable ability to "time travel" back to your childhood. An inner-child dialogue allows your childhood experiences to come to consciousness. You are then able to provide support and empathy for the child based on a true understanding of what the inner child experienced.

What the inner child may feel about the events of the past may not truly reflect what happened. There may be an element of over-exaggeration and embellishment. However, what's important is that it's true for the child and it should be accepted without judgment.

You will get better and better as you practice these conversations. You will become more at ease with acknowledging and listening to the concerns relayed by the inner child through your inner dialogue. Remember, that in order to change a long-established behavior pattern, the one that's making you feel stressed, you must first discover that pattern. Inner-child dialogues are the way to do just that.

The beliefs of the inner child won't change easily. You'll have to commit to repeated dialogues to see a real, meaningful difference in your stress levels and behavior. Try spending ten to fifteen minutes every day visiting with your inner child, perhaps before or after your meditation, or choose a separate time to drop in on what your inner child is thinking. Regular inner-child dialogues will make it much easier to use this technique during times of stress. Inner-child dialogues are the key to understanding why you react the way you do and once you understand "Why?" you can tackle the "How?" of change much easier.

## Practice

1. To truly understand the underpinnings of your own belief system, it's important to *consistently* dialogue with your inner child. Initially, dialogue on a daily basis until you begin to have a true insight into your own belief system. This is much easier to do when there's both time and privacy. You can do this when you're taking a walk alone, at night in bed before sleep, or you can set aside ten to fifteen minutes as a specific meditation practice.
2. You can also open an inner-child dialogue prior to your formal meditation practice.
3. Your mind is constantly talking to you so there's always an opportunity for discovery.
4. You can explore a previously challenging situation by just bringing up the memory of an emotionally charged event. It may seem commonplace, but every internal self-criticism is the doorway to understanding why you are the way you are.

## Summary

- You have an inner voice that is always commenting to you during times of stress and directing the action to be taken next.
- This voice is a pattern of response that it helps to think of as your inner child.
- The events in your life are filtered and interpreted by your inner child to determine how they fit with your internalized parental belief system and both you and the events are judged accordingly.
- Every child has experienced core wounding. This refers to childhood events, which were very emotionally traumatic and may have related to loss, rejection, abandonment, humiliation, betrayal and/or a sense of having been overwhelmed.

- As a child you responded to core-wounding events in a manner that made you feel less threatened and more comfortable, safe and accepted.
- As an adult your actions are still based on the same patterns that you developed as a child.
- Your behaviour is controlled by these unconscious, habitual childhood coping strategies (your inner child).
- By talking (i.e., having a dialogue) with your inner child, you can bring insight, empathy, support and love to the process of lessening the power that your childhood coping mechanisms have on your adult behaviour. This will help to reduce your stress levels.
- The inner-child dialogue is a process that allows you to discover your own, underlying belief system, explore its meaning and identify whether or not it's valid.
- To have an inner-child dialogue first bring mindfulness to your inner voice and listen to what it's saying. Then use the phrase *"My dear child..."* to help yourself to recognize that the inner voice isn't you but rather the voice of your belief system, the inner child. Engage in a conversation with the inner child and finally, begin the inquiry by asking it a series of questions.
- Ask, *"What is the feeling?"* *"What does bad/terrible/horrible really mean?"* *"What is the specific belief?"* and *"What does it mean to be safe, loveable and worthy?"* to discover some of the meaning behind the belief system.
- Examine if the belief system is true or valid by asking, *"Is it really that bad?"* *"Are you safe?"* *"Are you loveable and worthy?"* and finally, *"Is it fixable and if so what needs to be done?"*
- *"Why?"* is the most important word you'll use in your inner-child dialogue as you tailor the conversation to your own unique personal history.
- Reassure and support your inner child by asking what it needs to say to its caregivers as well as what it needs to hear from them.
- Use the daily habit of inner-child dialogue to gradually change the basis of your stress-reactions.

## 18

# Empathy for the Inner Child

I N THIS CHAPTER, YOU WILL LEARN how to use your adult perspective, along with a sense of empathy, to show your inner child a new way to look at its belief system. Having empathy for your inner child means that you understand and identify with the child's circumstances, motivations, and feelings. You'll learn how to use this understanding to determine what supportive actions you can take in order to begin a healing process that will ultimately result in a less reactive, less stressful approach to life.

## Reframing the Belief System of the Inner Child

The healing of the inner child comes from knowing that it has been truly heard, understood and supported. However, in order to make some effective change, there ultimately needs to be a reframing of the inner child's belief system. Reframing means that there needs to be a new way in which the child experiences the world.

To change the way your inner child experiences the world, you'll first use inner-child dialogue to discover the belief system that underlies your reactions and which determines how your inner child sees the world. Using further questioning, you'll examine if this belief system is true.

You'll likely discover that the belief system of the inner child is quite distorted and often views, even minor events, as catastrophic. Further examples of distorted beliefs include themes such as, love is conditional, you need to be perfect to be loved and you need to make your caregiver(s) happy to feel safe and worthy. After dialoguing with the child and discovering the distorted beliefs, you can then use that knowledge as a basis for reframing.

The child holds on to its beliefs very strongly. In examining the validity of the belief system you have already begun to challenge these beliefs. The next step is to demonstrate to your inner child that its belief system is not true and that there are other ways to look at the world. The process of reframing is simply the process of discovering these 'other ways', or alternate perspectives, and communicating them in a caring, empathic way to your inner child.

Larry and Mika examined what was learned from their inner-child dialogues and they were both able to come up with some alternate perspectives. These perspectives included:

- These are not terrible, catastrophic events.
- You don't need to be perfect to be loved.
- You are safe, loveable and worthy.
- You act from good intentions.
- You don't deserve to be hit.
- You don't deserve to be yelled at.
- You don't need to make your mother/father happy to feel safe.
- You have the right to ask for what you want.
- Problems can be solved.
- Everyone is responsible for his or her own feelings. You are not *making* your dad/mom happy or sad. He/she chooses that for himself/herself. You are a good person and don't intend to hurt anyone.
- You deserve to be heard.
- What you say matters.
- You are safe right now. There is no one here to hurt you.
- You are loveable even if you are not perfect.
- No one can control events.

The process of reframing, of discovering a new way of looking at things, and then communicating that to your inner child, will be unique to your experience. Your personal reframing process will reflect what you've learned from your inner-child dialogues. Reframing is an ongoing process of discovery and change.

## Choice

The inner child has unconditionally and blindly accepted its belief system as the truth. It never realized that there were other options. In exploring with the child that there may be other ways to look at a situation, the child, for the first time, may be able to realize that it *can choose what it believes. You* therefore, have a choice in what *you* believe.

In breaking down the old system, you have the opportunity to replace it with a new value system that is freeing, positive and uplifting. The new belief system often is the opposite of what the previous system was in many respects. Use your adult perspective to work on gradually replacing the parts of the old belief system that are causing you stress. Change the belief system by asking the inner child questions about each specific belief that comes up in your inner child dialogues. Ask:

- *Do you need to believe this anymore?*
- *Does believing this make you happy?*
- *What would it feel like if you didn't have to believe this anymore?*
- *Do you have a choice in what you believe?*
- *What's a different way to interpret this situation?*
- *What might a different belief sound like if you were to say it out loud?*
- *Do you think you could believe some part, if not all, of a different belief?*
- *Could you start to think even a little bit differently?*

# Actions and Affirmations

In addition to reinforcing for the child the idea that it has a choice about what to believe, there are actions and affirmations that you, as the adult, can offer your inner child to calm a sense of anxiety before it becomes an all-out stress reaction.

Imagine that a specific external event, or even an internal memory, has triggered your inner child to feel anxious and worried. It may have been an unpaid bill, what you said to a friend, forgetting to wish a friend a happy birthday, not exercising, cheating on a diet, buying a new shirt, necklace or phone, being overweight, getting angry, not getting angry, etc.

The child views itself as powerless and vulnerable. When a problem arises, the inner child doesn't feel that it's capable of dealing with it and starts to worry.

The adult presence can respond to the perceived cause of the child's anxiety by letting the child know that it will take care of the specific problem. This is a way of letting the child know that everything will be ok because you, as an adult, will be taking some action. The child will be safe as the adult is in control and has the ability to deal with whatever arises. Reassure the worried inner child by saying things such as:

*My dear child, thank you for reminding me. I will...pay the bill, make an effort to follow my diet, call my friend and wish her a happy birthday, get on my treadmill today etc.*

Actions can also involve the adult presence declaring how it will act on behalf of the inner child as it relates to its core-wounding issues. Be willing to give the inner child positive affirmations based on what it says that it needs. Positive affirmations are reassuring statements that describe a supportive action or feeling and generally begin with "I will..."

- I will keep you safe.
- I will love you unconditionally.

- I will speak on your behalf.
- I will not let people treat you disrespectfully.
- I will cherish you.
- I will listen to what you say without judgment.
- I will protect you when you feel afraid.
- I will stand up for you and speak on your behalf.

Everyone's inner child is different and what your inner child may specifically need to hear, in order to feel listened to, safe and validated will be unique. Perhaps your inner child may need to hear more reassurance regarding how difficult and unfair life was growing up. Perhaps the inner child needs to have its anger validated. Experiment and find out what works best for you.

Remember that your inner child is stuck in a time warp of sorts. It doesn't differentiate between the past and the present. Therefore, current supportive statements are accepted as if they are being heard in your actual childhood. For that reason, these affirmations have a powerful healing effect on the inner child that will quickly calm an anxious reaction.

It's important not to underestimate the power of self-directed loving-kindness in helping you to overcome your original core-wounding experiences, as well as your distorted personal belief system. Repeated statements of compassion, directed to the inner child, can rewire the way your brain works and allow for a more positive, automatic thought process.

It takes effort, dedication and time to see some real, permanent change but the outcome of a longer and less stressful life is worth it. Even baby steps in the right direction will help you feel better day-by-day. Begin your affirmations by reassuring yourself that, with perseverance and commitment, change will occur. Commit to changing the beliefs that make you stressed.

# Reclaiming the Voice of the Adult

For most of us, the dominant voice that comments on and controls our behaviors is the voice of the inner child. However, as we have discovered, this voice is based on a flawed belief system that originated in childhood. This belief system is not only unhelpful, but may be inappropriate for many current situations.

We have all evolved to a certain degree and we all have an adult presence. This adult is flawed, influenced by childhood coping strategies, but it's more wise, adaptable, capable and skillful than the inner child. It can see the exaggerated, and at times, inappropriate responses of the inner child and can bring a more reasoned response to a situation. Too often, we lose contact with the voice of the reasoning adult and operate only from the perspective of the inner child.

*You are creating a new relationship between the inner child and your present day adult through inner-child dialogue and empathy.* The aim of this relationship is to allow the child to know that it's supported, safe and loved. The child doesn't have to continue to live within the boundaries and coping strategies that it created in order to deal with the fears associated with its connection to its caregivers. Ultimately, your goal will be a direct and open communication between your inner child and the present day adult that you are now, rather than communication and control only happening through an automatic, unconscious, child-parent type of interaction.

Remember that the child feels afraid and vulnerable. It's frightened that it can't deal with a certain situation. It's important that a sense of *trust* is created in that the adult will be there to deal with whatever happens and will protect the child.

Typically, you live your life so much through the inner child that you lose the connection with your own adult voice. You are not powerless and you can remind yourself that you can be present in any situation from an adult perspective.

To do this, initially, before you speak or act in response to an emotional situation, you can ask yourself the question, *"Whose voice is this?"* or *"Is this my inner child or adult that's responding?"* This will at least make you aware of who's in control. Sometimes, it can be helpful to directly appeal to the adult within you by asking, *"What would a wiser adult do in this situation?"*

Before you speak or act, ask the valuable questions, *"Why am I doing this?"* and *"What's the purpose of this?"* When you start to question your motives, it quickly becomes apparent that you're either speaking or acting from a place that is intended to gratify your inner child, or from a place of a more mature and compassionate selflessness. Knowing this, you can then make a more rational decision about how you'd like to proceed.

Having identified your own core-wounding experiences as best you can, a more mature, adult response in an emotional situation may often be to simply *do nothing*. The inner child reacts to situations that trigger ancient memories. As an adult, you're now free to choose to live in the present. You can simply be present in the moment for what it is, uncluttered by what you believe it to be and the trappings of stories and reactions that are based on your childhood belief system.

You also have the ability to move beyond your conditioned adult presence and tap into a place of wisdom, understanding and compassion. Listen for your own voice of wisdom, which is your intuitive, knowing, wise awareness. It operates beyond the personal fears of your inner child and ego.

The voice of the adult is just a more conditioned, experienced reflex that has been progressively influenced by cultural, religious and secular values. The voice of wisdom is a more mature or ideal sensibility. It's important to your health and well-being that your behaviors be directed by mature, integrated and wholesome practices, rather than by the inner child's need to feel loved and accepted.

To be truly adult means to be present in this world from a place that doesn't need to satisfy childhood imperatives. Ideally, we would all strive to operate from a place of equanimity, fairness, justice, compassion and acceptance. This is a terribly lofty place that we can't always reach. However, we all have an internal, wise, knowing and intuitive self that we can tap into.

We have all experienced situations where we just know, instinctively, what fair and honest thing needs to be done. When you become aware of your own mental chatter, simply ask, *"What needs to be done now?"* This may access a part of your mind that isn't as self-focused, or "I" based and can start you on your way to reclaiming your adult voice from the din of your inner child's cries.

## Empathy in Everyday Life – Practice and Integration

Let's take everything that you've recently learned about inner-child dialogue, empathy and support and integrate it into a shorter version or summary dialogue, which you can use with your inner child during a stressful situation. To use a shortened version, you will need to have practiced the inner-child dialogue to the point where you have become quite familiar with your inner child and have a good idea of what your belief system is.

In the beginning, you'll need to practice a lot in order to become aware of what the child is experiencing and believes about particular types of events. You will discover that your child has its own unique core wounding and it uses the resulting coping strategies that it has developed (which you could also think of as defense mechanisms) over and over. Different events will trigger the same basic, common defense mechanisms. As you progress with your inner-child dialogues, you'll start to recognize these defense mechanisms and this will help you to shorten your inner-child dialogue so that you can use it to calm yourself during a stressful event.

Initially, it may be difficult to use the inner-child dialogue in the heat of the moment. Remember, that you can always review an emotional event later, when there's some time and privacy to have a dialogue. As you become more at ease and familiar with the process of dialoguing, you'll be able to use a shortened version of the dialogue, or even just a part of it, in the moment that an emotional or stressful event is occurring.

Here are the components of the shortened/summary dialogue:

1. **Awareness** of what's happening
2. **Acknowledgement of the feelings** of the inner child
3. **Stating** the belief system
4. **Reframing** the belief system
5. **Actions** on behalf of the child

## Awareness

Initially, describe to yourself, as objectively as you can, the stressful event that has occurred or that's currently unfolding. Give a simple description of what's happened and nothing more. This is a good way to frame the rest of the conversation that you'll have with your inner child. After describing the event as it initially presented itself, acknowledge the child's reaction to it.

> Coming back to the example of when Larry bought the suit, Larry would have described the initial event and his inner child's reaction by saying:
>
> *My dear child, you bought a suit that you think is too expensive.*

> Mika, in her situation, would have started with:
>
> *My dear child, you didn't bring the right file in and you're worried that you're not doing your job.*

## Acknowledge the Feeling

Step two is to acknowledge what emotion the inner child is feeling. Through your usual inner-child dialogue practice, you'll have a much quicker sense of what the inner child's core feeling is, in a given situation. If you don't have a sense of what the child is feeling, you can directly question the child and ask how it's feeling in the moment. Repeat what the inner child reports that it's feeling back to the child. This repetition is an acknowledgement that you know and understand what the child is feeling. This then lets the child know that it has been heard and understood.

Make sure that you don't judge the reported emotion as being good or bad. Just accept what the child says without any attempt to change it. If you were to discount, or minimize, the child's feelings by saying, "You're not sad. It's ok. Everything's good," the child would again be in a place wherein a dismissal of its feelings renders it powerless and invisible. Accepting what your inner voice is feeling will have the opposite effect. It will be empowering and uplifting.

In Larry's situation he would have said to his inner child:
*It sounds like you're feeling scared and angry.*

Mika would have made the comment:
*It sounds like you're feeling really nervous and worried.*

## Stating the Belief System

Your next step is to focus on the inner child's belief system. This step is important as it defines why the child is behaving the way it is. Bringing the underlying belief into the open, instead of leaving it where it normally hides beneath your conscious awareness, will start to shed some light on what the motivating force is for your actions.

State to your inner child what you think the child believes that is underlying its feelings and reactions. This isn't just a belief about a current stressful situation but a general core belief that you've run into before in your inner-child dialogues. Stating the core belief from the belief system, that's at work during a stress-reaction, will give you some additional clarity and a place to focus your attention in order to create change.

For this third step Larry might have said something like:
*You believe that if you make any mistake you will not be loved.*

Mika could have stated:
*You believe that you are not worthy and lovable. You believe that you need to make your dad happy to feel safe.*

## Reframing the Belief System

This forth step is a critical part of the shortened-dialogue process. In this step, you provide an alternate view of the belief system for the inner child. Remember, that looking at something in a different way is the beginning of the reframing process. Through your inner-child dialogues, you have discovered the inner child's belief system and from that discovery you are able to provide a more constructive way for the inner child to experience life. This reframing step is where you say something to the inner child that really challenges its beliefs.

Larry might have said:
  *My dear child you're loveable just as you are. You don't need to be perfect to be loved.*

Mika could have said:
  *My dear child, everyone is responsible for his or her own feelings. You are safe and worthy.*

## Actions

In the fifth and final step, the adult in you takes action. It provides words of support and empathy to your inner child. The child comes from a place of powerlessness and knowing that there are solutions to the perceived problem at hand is also reassuring. The adult can offer to act on these solutions. Additionally, if the child has said that it needs something in particular in order to feel reassured, the adult in you can specifically tailor some supportive statements to address those needs.

Larry might have chosen to say:
  *I am here for you. I will take care of you. I can work some overtime to pay for the suit.*

Mika could have said:
  *I will protect you. I love you no matter what you do. I will make sure that all the office work is done properly as best I can.*

Once again, the five steps, of a shortened inner-child dialogue that you can use right in the moment when you are feeling stressed, are:

1. **Awareness**: Describe the event in simple, direct language.
2. **Acknowledgement**: Say what emotion the inner child is feeling.
3. **State** the underlying belief from the inner child's belief system.
4. **Reframe** or challenge the child's beliefs by offering a different, more constructive way of looking at things.
5. **Actions**: Reassure the child with words of empathy and support. Tell the child what actions you will take to meet the child's needs, and if possible, what actions you'll take to fix the current problem.

Putting it all together, Larry would have said something like:

*My dear child, you bought a suit that you think is too expensive. It sounds like you're feeling scared and angry. You believe that if you make any mistake you will not be loved. You're loveable just as you are. You don't need to be perfect to be loved. I am here for you. I will take care of you. I can work some overtime to pay for the suit.*

Mika might have had a shortened, inner-child dialogue that sounded something like:

*My dear child you didn't bring the right work file in and you're worried that you're not doing your job. It sounds like you're feeling really nervous and worried. You believe that you're not worthy and lovable. You believe that you need to make your dad happy to feel safe. Everyone is responsible for his or her own feelings. You are safe and worthy. I will protect you. I love you no matter what you do. I will make sure that all the office work is done properly as best I can.*

As you become more and more familiar with your inner child and its underlying feelings and needs, providing the child with empathy and support will get faster and easier. This will really help to reduce your feelings of stress. It may not even be necessary to go through the whole process.

You'll find that certain parts of the process really work for you. With practice and regular inner-child dialogues, you'll be able to jump straight to the parts that are most helpful, that you feel strongly about, or that are just the quickest and most effective things to do and say in a crisis situation. You may only need to express an understanding of your inner child's feelings, or you may only need to quickly acknowledge the feeling and provide some reframing, or a supportive action statement.

Empathic support is essential for the healing of your inner child. What's said in order to provide this support is unique for each individual and depends on what's revealed in the on-going, inner-child dialogues. You'll need to practice inner-child dialogues on a daily basis, so that the core beliefs that are driving the child's reactions can be discovered.

It's important that the empathy that you express to your inner child is authentic, sincere and loving. Empty words will not work. Transformation of the inner child occurs because the child feels that it's loved unconditionally, and that it's respected and valued.

You have been too stressed for too long, but to transform a lifetime of stressful reactions overnight is not a reasonable expectation nor is it possible. You'll need to practice. You'll need to dialogue with your inner child. You'll need to challenge, reframe and transform a long-standing belief system that has been in operation since your early childhood. Above all, you'll need to be kind and compassionate with yourself as you journey toward a new belief system and a less stressful life.

## Practice

In order to become familiar with, and effective at, inner-child dialoguing, it's important to practice as often as you can.

**PRACTICING ON A DAILY BASIS IS ESSENTIAL!**

1. When you're in the middle of a conflict with another person, or when you're in the grip of an emotionally charged memory, it can be very difficult to start a dialogue where there is neither the privacy nor time. You may have to recognize that the inner child is present and upset and come back to the specific incident at a later time. The next time you're experiencing a stressful moment try saying something to yourself like, *"My dear child, I hear how scared you are. I'm here for you. Don't worry. You're safe, loveable and worthy. We'll talk later when there's more time."* You'll gradually discover what parts of the shortened/summary inner-child dialogue work best for you.

2. Inner-child dialogue must be practiced outside of a conflict or stressful situation. Have an empathic, inner-child dialogue in a formal (i.e., scheduled, daily practice) as well as informal (i.e., whenever you think of it) fashion, or ideally, do both. When you need to have an inner-child chat to reduce your stress in the heat of the moment, you'll be able to do much better the more you practice.

3. As a part of your formal practice, try starting a dialogue and see what spontaneously comes up. You could ask, *"My dear child, how are you feeling?"* Or you might choose to bring up an earlier, emotional memory. This can be done at a set time of the day such as, in the morning before getting out of bed, at night before going to sleep, before your daily meditation, or when you're out for a walk. Hold, even a brief dialogue, spontaneously, whenever you think of it.

4. You can also address a statement of support, from the conscious adult to the inner child, by using your reframing or action statements on a daily basis. The periodic statements of support can occur at formally scheduled times of the day, or you can provide them whenever you think of doing so. At those times, you might say something like, *"My dear child, you're safe, loveable and worthy. You don't have to be perfect to be loved. I accept and love you just as you are."* Write down some supportive statements that you can use throughout the day.

5. It's helpful to connect with the inner child everyday and just ask how the child is feeling. Give it the time and opportunity to express itself. Simply listen, and then provide support. More regular contact will make it easier to perform this behavioral-change and stress-reduction technique during times of crisis.

## Summary

- The healing of the inner child comes from the feeling that it's been truly heard. Just listening to what the child needs to say is therapeutic.
- Having empathy for your inner child means that you understand and identify with the child's circumstances, motivations, and feelings.
- The process of developing and expressing this empathy includes: **Awareness** of what's being said and who's saying it, **Acknowledgment of the feelings** of the inner child, an **Exploration** of the belief system, **Reframing** the belief system and **Actions** on behalf of the child.
- Expressing empathy for the inner child is part of a process of transforming the core beliefs of the child from something that's causing you considerable stress to something that's more helpful and constructive in your daily life. This important transformation is called reframing.
- You have a choice in what you believe. You are creating a new relationship between the inner child and your present day adult through inner-child dialogue and empathy.
- To change the way your inner child reacts to situations, you'll first use inner-child dialogue to discover the belief system that underlies these reactions. Using further questioning, you'll examine if this belief system is true. After dialoguing with the child and discovering its distorted beliefs, you can then use that knowledge as a basis for changing the beliefs that are causing your stress.

- Here are the steps to a shortened version of an inner-child dialogue that you can use in times of stress:

  1. Describe what happened that made you feel stressed;
  2. Say what emotion the inner child is feeling;
  3. State the underlying belief from the inner child's belief system;
  4. Reframe the child's beliefs by offering a different perspective;
  5. Provide reassurance, empathy and support and tell the child what actions you'll be taking to meet the child's needs, as well as what you're going to do to deal with the current problem.

# 19

## Empathy For Others

WHEN YOU RECOGNIZE THAT THERE'S a wounded child behind your inner voice's judgments and criticisms, it becomes apparent that you aren't the only one who is acting according to habits and patterns developed in childhood. We all share the same fundamental humanity, which invariably includes core-wounding experiences to a greater or lesser degree. This knowledge will hopefully allow you to understand, to some extent, why people act the way they do. This will also allow you to look beyond their actions to the motivating factors beneath them. You can now view other people with more compassion, knowing that they too have an inner child that has suffered.

As you direct a conversation with your inner child, encourage the child to see that it's not alone in the world and that there's an inner child in every person. Keep this in mind and try to extend more understanding, patience and empathy to those around you.

It's also very important for you to recognize that we all have inner-child core wounding and therefore we operate as adults using unconscious, child-created coping strategies in order to live in this world. On the surface, what someone else might say or do may seem insensitive and cruel, but if you truly understood the motives for that person's actions, you would likely be more compassionate and less reactive.

The experience of the inner child's core wounding is universal and joins each of us at the heart. Because of this, it may be possible to connect directly from your inner child to the inner child of another person. With this type of connection there is no judgment or competition. There is only a heartfelt intimacy. This intimacy allows you to transcend the normal reaction of taking everything as a personal attack.

The next time you're in a conversation with another person, especially where there is conflict, you'll find that you can quickly develop a sense of empathy by thinking, *"How is this person's inner child suffering?"* or *"What needs to be said to this person's inner child?"* Just as you have an inner child that's trying to be loved and accepted, so too does this other person. He or she is communicating in a way that simply reflects that individual's personal strategies for survival, which are, in turn, based on his or her previous experiences as a frightened child.

Here is a conversation that shows how you might demonstrate to your inner child the universal nature of the core wounding that connects us all:

Mika's inner voice is talking to her again but this time it's out loud. She's on a diet and has cheated again. This is a repeated theme for her.

Mika's inner voice says:

*How could I have done this? I know better. I can never get this dieting thing right. I am horrible!*

Your adult says:

*My dear child why are you horrible?*

Mika's inner child:

*I am always getting things wrong. I am always making a mistake. It's not good to make a mistake.*

Your adult questions:

*Why is it not good to make a mistake?*

Mika's inner voice answers:

*My mother was always criticizing me for being fat. She would never just accept me for who I was. I always had to be thin, good at school, good at sports and good at home. If I wasn't, then I could feel her disapproval. I really am angry with her!*

Your adult responds:

*Why are you so angry with your mother?*

Mika answers as the feelings begin to well up from her inner child's experiences:

*You're darn right. I am angry! She would never let me be me. I always had to be the way she wanted me to be!*

You ask:

*Why do you think she acted that way?*

Mika's inner voice responds:

*Well she had a pretty tough life. Her father died when she was young and she had to go to work and drop out of school for a while. She never got over his death. I have to give her credit. She worked very hard to accomplish the things she did.*

You question:

*Do you think she could be scared too?*

Mika's inner child says:

*You know, you're probably right. She always felt that it was important to be as good as you could be. She had a pretty tough life and she felt that the way to succeed was to work really hard in everything you do.*

You respond:

*Do you think she also had an inner child and that part of her is still trying to meet the expectations of her own parents? Is there another way you can look at her?*

Mika is beginning to feel better and says:

*I could try to look at her a different way and maybe be more understanding.*

In this hypothetical conversation, Mika's inner child was led to the insight that everyone has an inner child that has suffered. Coming to this realization creates a greater understanding and compassion for others.

Empathy for others, as expressed through an inner-child-to-inner-child connection can also occur in a non-verbal way. For example, recently I was having a conversation with a patient and she mentioned how she felt unaccepted and unworthy in her family. As the conversation continued, I began to relate to her, not from my adult-doctor perspective, but from the place of my own injured child, who could identify with her experience. I felt compassion and a very fundamental connection with her. At the end of the conversation, she said that this was the first time that she had been able to really share her story. I believe that we had subconsciously connected on an inner child level.

When you recognize that we are all the same in that we view much of life through our childhood filters, there can be a greater opportunity to connect in a deeper way with your fellow human beings. The next time you're having an emotional conversation, try to be aware of the fact that the other person is talking to you from the perspective of his or her inner child and its related core wounding. As you take a moment to consider the childhood origins of his or her perspective, words or actions, try to allow a more intimate inner-child-to-inner-child connection to occur. Don't take things so personally.

## Practice

1. The next time you have a conversation with some good friends or loved ones, see if you can think of them as having an inner child and try to find out what needs they have that are not being met.
2. Before you continue to react in your next emotional situation, ask yourself, *"Is this my inner child or adult that's responding?"* This will at least make you aware of who's in control.

## Summary

- Everyone has their own inner child who has suffered some emotionally traumatic, core-wounding experiences.
- Empathy is the ability to identify with the point-of-view, feelings and attitudes of another person. Bring empathy to your conversations with others and recognize each person's inner child in order to extend compassion and understanding to your relationships.

- It's possible to connect directly from your inner child to the inner child of another person to create a deep intimacy, which may stop you from viewing that person's words as a personal attack.

# 20

# Mindfulness of the Inner Child: Putting It All Together

OW LET'S PUT THE PRINCIPLES OF MINDFULNESS and the concept of dialoguing with your inner child together, into one concise, comprehensive and clear practice.

Mindfulness is the practice of just being present to what arises from a place of compassion, acceptance and wisdom. There's no need to change what arises. However, awareness and being present with what arises are *not* enough to free you from the stressful thoughts that can take over your mind. When the mind-states (i.e., emotions) of anger, sadness, fear, etc. arise, you can probably now recognize that they're present, but you still likely identify with them. You believe what you experience, not realizing that it's really an illusion, an interpretation created in the moment by your inner child. This leads to suffering and stress.

Freedom from stress comes from practicing mindfulness, in order to be aware of your own thought processes, and then combining this mindfulness with inner-child dialogues to discover how your mind creates its sense of reality. When you understand the whole process and have insight into the belief system and needs of your inner child, you can begin to reframe, or change, those beliefs. You can calm your inner child, change how you see the world and how you react to it, and in the process, begin to live life with less stress on your plate.

Mindfulness of your thought processes allows you to connect the dots and see the stories that are created from the original sensation or event. You never directly experience something. Inner-child dialogue reveals that you, along with everyone else in the world, are a wounded child operating from a need to feel loved and worthy.

The best coping strategies, those that you unconsciously use, arose in your childhood. The inner critic is just your inner child trying to cope.

Wisdom comes from seeing how your mind constructs its experiences. The mind creates stories and there's no one doing this but your conditioned belief system. When you realize that you're operating from a four-year-old's perspective, you'll start to feel that initial sense of freedom. You don't have to listen to your own inner critic. You are free to feel and behave differently.

Understanding this invaluable truth takes time and practice as outlined in this book. It's a progressive practice that starts with mindfulness of experience, which is just an awareness of what's happening. Next, there's mindfulness of process, which allows you to see the mind's stories and how you relate to them. Inner-child dialogue then lets you discover the origins of your belief system and finally empathy gives you a chance to reframe and reconstruct the experiences, emotions and expressions that imprinted themselves on your childhood. Ultimately, wisdom and freedom come from knowing that the mind's sense of reality is a fabrication, empty of truth.

So to put all that you've learned together, let's use the letters **A**, **B**, **C**, **D** and **E** once again. You first used these letters to remind you how to be mindful of your breath, but now you'll use them as a final overview of your stress-reduction strategy. Here is the essence of your daily practice:

- **A** is for **Awareness** – What's happening?
- **B** is for **Body and Breath** – What physical sensations are present?
- **C** is for **Connection** – What's fact and what's story?
- **D** is for **Dialogue** – Talk to your inner child.
- **E** is for **Empathy** – Reframe the belief system and support the inner child.

# A is for Awareness

Whenever you can remember to do so, ask yourself, *"What's happening?"*

This first step is always *Awareness* or *Mindfulness* of what's happening. You're often sleepwalking through your life. Anytime something pops into your mind, you believe that this is who you are and you react automatically and unconsciously according to the conditioned belief system of the inner child. You're like a puppet controlled by the invisible strings of your belief system, as voiced and acted upon by your inner child. You can become angry, sad, anxious, happy etc. and not even know how you're behaving, let alone why you're behaving that way.

The hardest part of mindfulness is remembering to be mindful. Your mind starts telling stories and it's so easy to get carried away. Stop and observe. The best way to do this is by asking yourself questions. Ask yourself, *"What's happening?"* The question will snap you instantly back into the present moment, and pull you out of the story that you're starting to tell yourself.

It's important to remember that what you're asking is, *"What's happening?"* and not *"What am I experiencing?"* so that you're taking the word, as well as the concept, of "I" out of the experience. You're just noticing what's going on from the position of the observer rather than from the vantage point of the star of the show.

In response to this question, in traditional mindfulness, you'd *label* the experience objectively using the form, *"now anger,"* *"now sadness,"* *"now worry"* etc. It's important not to personalize what's happening by using "I" as in, *"I am..."* or *"I feel..."*. When you use "I" to describe your experiences, your stories will get more and more complex and you'll feel more stressed. It helps to remember that you're bringing your awareness to a state of mind.

Understand, that mindfulness is an accepting process. It's counterproductive to clamp down and tightly hold on to the sensation that you're experiencing. In mindfulness, you're receiving everything with a vast and open mind and then letting it go. It's important that you receive sensations into this spacious awareness. Relate to any experience from a place of acceptance and *'knowing'*. How you anchor yourself, or how you relate to any experience, is simply by being conscious of it with this spacious awareness. Don't let the "I "of the inner child make everything so personal. Just give yourself the freedom to experience a sensation, accept it and let it go.

If you have already had some inner-child dialogues, you may have discovered the underlying core feeling behind many of your emotional reactions. Recall, that the inner child may be feeling quite fearful, nervous or even angry if something is triggering a reaction that's based on a bad experience, a core-wounding experience, from your childhood. You may want to label this core feeling directly such as *"now fear"* instead of only acknowledging the feelings that first came into your awareness. In other words, let your awareness dig deeper as you ask yourself, *"What's happening?"*

You could also bring your awareness to what's being said by the inner voice during a stressful moment. Just listen intently and follow the words without identifying with them. If you can focus your attention on what your inner voice is saying, this focus will stop you from spiraling into a more exaggerated emotional response. You'll be less likely to identify with the story that your mind is inventing. The emotional state of mind will ultimately disappear and take your stress with it.

Recognize that the inner voice of your stories is that of your inner child and not your adult, or wiser self. This will make it easier for you to mentally stand back and observe.

Anchor your awareness of the inner child by asking, *"Whose voice is this?"* Bring your attention to the words of your inner voice and listen to the voice for as long as it needs to speak. Let your inner child know that you're there by saying, *"My dear child, I hear you."*

Use cues such as those trusty Post-it notes, alarms, regular activities, or times of day etc. to remind you to be mindful of your environment, your experience and the voice of your inner child. Bring your awareness to what's happening in the moment. Be mindful whenever you can and it will be easier to be mindful when you find yourself in a stressful situation.

# B is for Body and Breath

Now that you've brought your awareness to what's happening with your inner child and what you're feeling emotionally, it's time to expand your awareness of your experience to include your *body*.

Ask yourself the question, *"What physical sensations are present?"*

What you're after here is what's happening in the *body*. How are the mental and emotional states that are occurring being expressed as a physical sensation? Ground your attention in the physical sensations in order to step out of the storyline and depersonalize the experience. You'll realize that it's not an "I" that's upset, but only a squeezing sensation that's being experienced.

Rest in the mental, emotional and physical totality of the experience and just be with whatever presents itself. Learn how sadness, fear, anger, or happiness feels for you personally, in your body as well as your mind.

Expand your physical awareness by recognizing that what's being experienced represents the way your inner child is feeling in the moment, how your inner child experiences life. Once you've explored, and truly understood, the origins of the belief system of your inner child through dialoguing, mindfully observing how the inner child is reacting in any given moment may be all you need to do. This can be done on a moment-to-moment basis with the application of ongoing mindfulness.

Also, remember that the *breath* is part of the body. When you become aware of a thought, emotion or physical feeling, use this awareness as a *cue* to bring mindfulness to the breath. Notice what's happening to your breathing. When you're tense the breath may become short or uneven, or you may even hold your breath. Bring mindfulness to your breath, and with observation, it will likely become much calmer. Remember, that with mindfulness you just follow the breath without trying to change it.

If you're feeling very stressed, then you may need to consciously breathe in a slow, deep, quiet, smooth fashion, from your diaphragm, emphasizing your exhalations. The letters **A**, **B**, **C**, **D** and **E** can also be used to remind you of how to breathe in a calm manner (have an

**Awareness** of the breath, **B**reathe **C**almly, practice **D**iaphragmatic breathing and emphasize the **E**xhalation). A calmer breath leads to a calmer mind.

The more you can bring mindfulness to your breath throughout the day, the more relaxed you'll feel. You'll be using an internal cue, in this case your breathing, to in turn, prompt your mindfulness.

The breath supports every moment of mindfulness. When you become aware of a sensation, bring your attention to your breath and either observe it mindfully, or choose to consciously breathe in a more effective way. This will help support your mindfulness and decrease your stress-response. If you remember nothing else in a stressful moment, remember to use your breathing to calm your mind and your body. Controlling your breathing helps to dampen an emotional or stressful response.

In difficult situations, you can *count your breaths* to help keep you focused on your breathing. The first breath in and out counts as one, the next breath in and out counts as two etc.

Connect the breath and the body to calm down. When you're feeling discomfort, tension, or pain, imagine breathing into and out of the specific spot that's bothering you in order to calm the area. Continue to breathe in this fashion until the tension or discomfort passes. When stressed, you can imagine that as you breathe in, you're drawing all the negative energy of the moment to a small point and then exhaling it out of your body.

Some stressful mental events don't have much substance or energy behind them. Just bringing your awareness to them is often enough to cause them to vanish. There will be lots of experiences that are quite emotional for you and you'll have to use more of the techniques discussed in this book in order to handle them in the best way possible. For example, make use of the specific relaxation practices such as the *Body Scan* and *Progressive Muscle Relaxation* techniques.

# C is for Connection

*What's the connection between the original fact, sensation or event and how you're feeling?* In other words, *what's fact and what's story?* When you start to figure out the connection between fact and fiction; the fiction being the story that you told yourself that made you feel upset, you are acting as a Sherlock Holmes in your own mind, following the process and clues from point a to point b.

Mindfulness practitioners often say to "just let go" of the stressful thought. This can be a very difficult thing to do if you're identifying with whatever comes up. Following the process of mental activity shifts the perspective and allows you to view the mind with curiosity and interest. You can step out of the storyline and be the observer without owning the content.

If the stressful thought or emotion is powerful, then bring awareness to the process of how the mind functions. When you react to an event, it takes place on two levels. The first level is the apparent, present-day-adult reaction. The second level is the deeper, underlying reaction of the inner child. This deeper reaction is based on the core belief system that you developed as a survival mechanism when you were a child. You react according to how you've filtered what's actually occurring, through your belief system.

Bring awareness to the story you're telling yourself, in order to defuse the intensity of your reaction. Be aware of your core belief system, and how your reactions arise when you behave in a manner that conflicts with it. You'll be able to change your reaction using the wisdom of this insight.

Ask, *"What's the fact?"* and *"What's the story?"* Identify the original thought and then the reaction. Witness how your mind creates wild and unbelievable stories about everything and it will be easier for you to let go of the story. Let go of the story and the stress will lessen or disappear entirely. As you gain more experience in practicing mindfulness of process, just bringing your attention to the initial fact, event, or sensation may help prevent the story from expanding out of control.

Your mind uses your belief system to try to figure out whether or not what you're experiencing is safe or dangerous. Stories are then created about what you experience and you relate to the story and not to the original sensation or occurrence. If you can engage your mind in the task of identifying this process, you step out of the storyline and give yourself some mental distance. You become the objective witness. It also allows you to see the empty nature of your thoughts, in that you are actually reacting to a fictional story.

The connection between *the fact* and *the story* is important for identifying how your mind processes what you experience and judges you for *what* you did or didn't do. Inner-child dialogue helps you understand some of the reasons for your actions and offers another way to approach your thoughts. Focus on *why* you did or didn't do something and why you feel the need to judge yourself, instead of *what* you did. This will undermine the stress-response taking place in your mind.

Here's an example of how you can reduce a stress-response by focusing on *why* you chose to do something, as opposed to *what* you did. My patient Larry needed some help from a co-worker but he had been raised never to ask for anything. His parents always rejected his requests and made him feel invisible and not worthy enough to ask for anything. Feeling stressed, Larry mindfully noticed his inner voice criticizing him for his inaction. His stress dissipated as he examined why he wasn't able to ask for help. Larry shifted his attention from what he had or hadn't done, to the workings of his inner child and its conditioned responses.

Compassion is more easily expressed when you are reminded of the inner child's core wounding and what strategies the child uses to cope. In Larry's case, his inner child's strategy was simply to not ask for any help no matter what. Once you identify the connection between fact and story you can ask yourself, "*Why did I do or not do this?*" or "*Why is there a need to judge myself?*" If you are still troubled after this process, you can ask yourself, "*What's my relationship to this story?*" The real suffering isn't in the story itself but in claiming ownership of it, identifying with it, and then building on it. If you can be present to the story and say that it's "*not who I am,*" then the story remains a mental event and not something that defines you. Examine this relationship objectively to create space around what's happening and give yourself more time to choose how you want to react.

In response to, *"What's my relationship to this story?"* the answer could be, *"Looks like I'm claiming ownership"* or *"I'm just observing this story and not owning it."* Examine how you're relating to the story. If there's ownership happening, that is you notice yourself using a lot of "I" statements, then in knowing this, it may allow you to more consciously see the connection and not be carried along in an automatic and unconscious thought process.

Finally, ask yourself, *"What would it feel like if I could let go of this thought?"* You're asking your mind to perform a task that it naturally knows how to do. Just allow this to happen without getting in the way. Don't purposely try to let go.

# D is for Dialogue

Mindfulness is a wonderful technique that brings you into the present moment more fully, without having to change it or own it, in order to reduce the stress that comes from focusing on the past or the future. However, I have discovered that it can be difficult for people to let go of what their inner voices are saying, so that they can be fully aware of what's happening in the present.

If this is true for you, through inner-child dialogue you can develop insight into the origins of your inner voice, the one that tries to direct everything. You'll come to recognize that this voice is your inner child trying to feel safe. Everything is judged against the inner child's belief system, so that the child can feel safe, worthy and loveable. Recognize this and the voice will have less energy to control your behavior.

When dialoguing with your inner child, be accepting and open. You are trying to discover what the inner child is feeling and believing. Use open-ended questions (questions that can't be answered by saying "yes" or "no") that begin with *"Why..."*.

Dialoguing involves a certain sequence of steps, which you should review regularly until you really get the hang of it. These steps are:

1. Mindfulness – Bring awareness to your inner voice.
2. "My dear child..." – Recognize that your inner voice isn't you.
3. Engage – Start a conversation with yourself.
4. Inquire – Ask some questions that take the form of "Why...?"

The first step is to bring awareness to what you're experiencing. However, inner-child dialogue is invaluable for understanding why you're feeling the way you are. It brings light to the whole conditioned process so that you can transform and reframe it. When you're angry, sad, frightened etc., don't just be angry, sad, or frightened. Remember to take the next step and explore why you are feeling the way you are.

The purpose of the inner-child dialogue is to discover the underlying core belief system, explore if it's true and identify the child's feelings. With practice, you'll begin to change this belief system and heal the inner child so that you'll be less reactive and less stressed in your daily life.

Sometimes there are no words for it but you just feel uneasy physically or emotionally. This is yet another occasion for you to hold an inner-child dialogue. Ask open-ended questions that can't be answered with a simple "yes" or "no" response. Listen. Don't judge or want to solve the problem. Allow the dialogue to unfold naturally. Remember, the most important word that you'll be using is *"Why...".*

Dialogue about whatever presents itself in the moment. If you can't have an inner-child dialogue because you're in public, bring up the memory of the event and your reaction to it, later, when there's privacy and time. To realize the most benefits from dialoguing with your inner child, practice on a regular basis.

# E is for Empathy

It's vital that you bring a sense of empathy, compassion and understanding to your inner-child dialogues. After you have been having regular inner-child dialogues for a while, you'll have discovered what the child's belief system is and what it needs to feel safe, loved and worthy. With this knowledge, you'll begin to reframe the belief system. This reframing is basically just offering a different perspective, an alternate way to view life, so that the child will progressively have a more constructive, positive and healthier belief system.

You, as the voice of the adult, can repeat positive affirmations (positive statements that are personal, reassuring and uplifting) or action statements that reflect what you intend to do in order to finally meet the inner child's previously unmet feelings and needs. The child is powerless but the adult can act on the child's behalf. The adult in you can confirm that, as much as is possible, you'll do what needs to be done in order to take care of whatever is worrying the child.

You'll begin to feel a sense of relief as the inner child starts to feel better as a consequence of knowing that it's being understood and supported. Through empathic support, you'll have the ability to transform the inner child's reactions and you'll experience less stress as a result. The child learns that it's safe, loveable and worthy.

Finally, you can provide a summary of a troubling event to the inner child. You can jump right to this shortened version, or summary, if you don't have time to hold a longer dialogue during a stressful event. Here's what you need to do in a shortened, or summary version, of an inner-child dialogue:

- Describe the event
- Express what the inner child is feeling
- State the belief
- Provide some reframing
- State the actions and positive affirmations

Do the shortened dialogue throughout the day or when you encounter troubling feelings, thoughts or events. The complete process of Awareness, Body and Breath, Connection, Dialogue and Empathy should still be practiced when there's time and privacy to do so. It's important to create a formal designated time to practice inner-child dialoguing and to do it as often as you can. You'll need to hold frequent dialogues in order to become familiar with the core wounding, coping strategies and needs of your inner child.

# Other Approaches to Stress (Minding your Mind)

Stress is an issue. Reducing your stress is work. It takes knowledge, practice and commitment. However, the real issue is how you deal with your mind on a moment-to-moment basis during a stressful event.

- At the very least, you need to be as mindful, or as aware, of what's being experienced as possible. What mental, emotional and physical state is present?
- Next, make use of the breath as an effective and immediate tool to provide you with some relaxation and dampen your automatic, over-reactive responses. You can either bring your attention to the breath or intentionally breathe in a relaxed manner.

This, initially, may be all that you can do in the heat of a really stressful moment. However, as you become more experienced in the practice of mindfulness and more familiar with the inner child and its underlying feelings and needs, you'll be able to apply some of the other techniques that you've learned. Give different techniques a try until you find out what's most effective for you. Try one or more of the following approaches during a stressful moment, but remember that they'll all be much more effective and easier to do if you're regularly practicing, mindfulness, relaxed breathing, and inner-child dialoguing:

- Bring your attention to the *physical sensations* and rest in the body knowing that you're directly experiencing how the inner child feels. All sensations are impermanent and will ultimately pass.
- Look for the *connection* between the initial fact or sensation and the story. Mindfulness of your thought process is a wonderful way to step out of the storyline and bring awareness to how your mind works. Remember, the story that Larry told himself:

*I bought the suit and now I'm terrible and will be penniless.*

It was Larry's story that was stressful, not the fact that he bought a suit.

- Examine how you're *relating* to the mental state that's present. Are you grabbing on to the story and identifying with it or letting it go?

- Acknowledge the *presence of the inner child* by saying:

  *My dear child, I hear you.*

- Create a *dialogue* with the child:

  *Why is this (terrible, bad, scary... etc.)?*

- Acknowledge the *feelings* of the child:

  *My dear child, you seem (frightened, sad, angry...).*

- Identify the *belief system*:

  *You believe that if you make a mistake you're not loveable.*

- Provide *reframing*:

  *You don't need to be perfect to be loved.*

- State the relevant *affirmations* and *actions* that you're willing to take to help:

  *I will support you, love and protect you. I will make sure all the work is done.*

Once you've been practicing mindfulness and inner-child dialogue for some time and have truly begun to understand that the stressful mental states that you're experiencing are fabrications of the mind, invented stories based on your childhood belief system, you can be present in any given moment in a very freeing way. The qualities of any internal or external stressful sensation or event that you experience are all creations of your mind.

Stress is an interpretation. It's not part of the original sensation itself. Stress is produced by your reaction in the moment, as you gauge everything you experience according to your belief system. When you experience something that you're interpreting as stressful, say to yourself:

- *This is a fabrication, a story of the mind, and I choose not to believe it.*
  or
- *Do I want to live my life according to the conditioned belief system of my inner child?*
  or
- *I choose to do nothing right now. I will just rest in the knowledge that the mental state that I'm experiencing is an illusion of the mind.*

As the last important step in your integrated practice, I want you to consider how you act toward others. There's always an element of "I" present in whatever you do. The question is whether this is a dominant motivation in how you behave, or whether a more universal, compassionate, connected perspective dictates your behaviour.

As you start to see the illusory nature of how the mind constructs its suffering, based on the conditioned reality of the inner child, there's less to defend and your heart can open. You'll understand that we all act from a wounded beginning. There's a universal, underlying sense of fear that connects us all.

You don't have to act from a place of always having to defend your inner child. Before you speak or act, ask yourself, *"Why am I doing this?"* or *"What's the purpose of this?"* You can then consciously decide whether you're making the best choice for yourself as well as others. Your inner wisdom and heart intuitively know the wisest way to act. You can engage this inner wisdom by asking yourself, *"What needs to be done now?"* In your heart, you'll know the answer.

# 21

## Some Final Thoughts

I THINK THAT WE CAN ALL AGREE that life is stressful and we all want to be a little bit happier in our day-to-day experiences. Some might define happiness as having more things, but for me, it's being able to be present for whatever my mind poses to me, without automatically and unconsciously reacting in a fearful, angry or anxious way.

I ask myself, "What's my goal in life?" The answer has changed over the years, but currently, I desire to be fully present in each moment with awareness, joy, gratitude, interest, acceptance, insight and wisdom. I want to be present from an openness of heart that doesn't need to defend my ego or my inner child. If there's nothing to defend, then there's nothing to fear. I can feel connected to the world in an understanding and compassionate way. I want to be *fearless*.

I have explored many different spiritual and psychological traditions in my own personal quest to find greater happiness. I have found that the ability to have an inner-child dialogue, as a way to understand the core motivation for how my mind works, along with the ability to hold the experience mindfully, to be complementary and transformative techniques.

I encourage you to view each moment of awareness, whether it's perceived to be good or bad, as a gift. Each is a wonderful opportunity to see how your mind works. Every moment of mindfulness brings you a step closer to freedom from stress and suffering. When I say, "My dear child, I hear you." I always smile, as I'm happy that I'm listening to my inner child and bringing mindfulness to the moment.

The inner child is an integral part of who we are. You are not trying to change, deny or eliminate it. The goal is to bring awareness to the inner child and hold it with the compassion and spaciousness of mindfulness. It can then pass through your awareness without you identifying with it. You are just changing the relationship you have with the inner child.

It's quite amazing how our minds function. There's the automatic, primal consciousness of what comes into awareness. Our minds are capable of being angry, sad or happy and we identify with and then tend to become those emotional and mental states. However, we also have the ability to be aware of what we are aware of. We can be mindful without necessarily reacting.

The mind has two basic mental states when it all comes down to it. One leads to stress and suffering and the other to an open acceptance, without the ownership and grief, of whatever is currently happening. Why do we choose the mental state that causes so much grief? I believe that it's because we're not aware that we can choose to operate from a different perspective. We haven't learned that we can use mindfulness and inner-child dialogue to deal with the unconscious, conditioned, coping strategies of the wounded inner child. Freedom from stress ultimately comes from observing that suffering is really a mental construction, and that means you're free to change it.

I have tried to outline some practical approaches to lasting stress reduction so that, at the end of the day, you have some excellent techniques to work with. However, you may have experienced significant trauma in your life and it's important to seek additional professional help under those circumstances.

Even with all the work we do, we will always carry the legacies of our childhood scars. Hopefully, what you can expect is that, although you may never be free from your childhood memories and their effects, you will have learned ways to cope. You'll have learned to be free to have had those earlier experiences without them seriously interfering with your ability to enjoy life now.

The beautiful union of mindfully observing the inner-child experience and using inquiry and inner-child dialogue to reframe it, allows for insight, wisdom and finally freedom, from the automatic and often stressful functioning of the mind.

I wish you well and I hope that, in some way, this book has been of value to you. It has certainly been a tremendously worthwhile experience for me. It's a very liberating experience to try to understand our minds and how we operate in this world. On the road of life, it really is nice to have a driver's manual.

*Namaste!*

*Phil Blustein, MD*
*Calgary, Alberta*
*December, 2014*

# Suggestions for Further Reading

Altman, D. (2010). *The mindfulness code.* Novato, CA: New World Library.

Bhikkhu, B. (1997). *Mindfulness with breathing.* Boston, MA: Wisdom Publications.

Brach, T. (2003). *Radical acceptance: Embracing your life with a heart of a Buddha.* New York, NY: Bantam-Dell.

Catherine, S. (2008). *Focused and fearless.* Boston, MA: Wisdom Publications.

Chodron, P. (1997). *When things fall apart.* Boston, MA: Shambhala.

Chopich, E. & Paul, M. (1990). *Healing your aloneness: Finding love and wholeness through your inner child.* San Francisco, CA: Harper San Francisco.

Coleman, M. (2006). *Awake in the wild.* Maui, HI: Inner Ocean Publishing.

Cousins, N. (2001). *Anatomy of an illness.* New York, NY: W.W. Norton.

Dalai Lama & Cutler, H. (1998). *The art of happiness.* New York, NY: Riverhead.

Epstein, M. (2001). *Going on being.* New York, NY: Broadway Books.

Epstein, M. (1998). *Going to pieces without falling apart.* New York, NY: Broadway Books.

Epstein, M. (1995). *Thoughts without a thinker: Psychotherapy from a Buddhist perspective.* New York, NY: Basic Books.

Flickstein, M. (2001). *Swallowing the river Ganges: A practical guide to the path of purification.* Boston, MA: Wisdom Publications.

Fronsdal, G. (2008). *The issue at hand: Essays on buddhist mindfulness practice (2nd edition).* Redwood City, CA: Insight Meditation Centre.

Goldstein, J. (2002). *One dharma.* New York, NY: Harper San Francisco.

Goldstein, J. & Kornfield, J. (1987). *Seeking the heart of wisdom.* Boston, MA: Shambhala Publications.

Gordon, T. (1975). *P.E.T. – parent effectiveness training.* New York, NY: New American Library.

Gunaratana, H. (1993). *Mindfulness in plain English.* Boston, MA: Wisdom.

Hagen, S. (2003). *Buddhism is not what you think.* New York, NY: Harper San Francisco.

Hanh, T.N. (1975). *The miracle of mindfulness.* Boston, MA: Beacon Press.

Kabat-Zinn, J. (1997). *Wherever you go there you are.* New York, NY: Hyperion.

Kabat-Zinn, J. (1990). *Full catastrophe living.* New York, NY: Dell.

Kornfield, J. (2008). *The wise heart.* New York, NY: Bantam Books.

Kornfield, J. (2000). *After the ecstasy, the laundry.* New York, NY: Bantam Books.

Kyabgon, T. (2003). *Mind at ease.* Boston, MA: Shambhala Publications.

Kushner, H. (1996). *How good do we have to be?* Boston, MA: Back Bay Books.

Levine, N. (2007). *Against the stream: A buddhist manual for spiritual revolutionaries.* New York, NY: Harper Collins.

Mipham, S. (2003). *Turning the mind into an ally.* New York, NY: Riverhead Books.

Moffitt, P. (2008). *Dancing with life: Buddhist insights for finding meaning and joy in the face of suffering.* New York, NY: Rodale Books.

Paul, M. (1992). *Inner bonding: Becoming a loving adult to your inner child.* San Francisco, CA: Harper.

Perls, F. (1969). *Gestalt therapy verbatim.* Moab, UT: Real People Press.

Pollard, J.K. (1987). *Self parenting: The complete guide to your inner conversations.* Malibu, CA: Generic Human Studies Publishing.

Rinpoche, S. (1992). *The Tibetan book of living and dying.* San Francisco, CA: Harper.

Rinpoche, T. (2003). *Fearless simplicity.* Hong Kong, HK: Rangjung Yeshe Publications.

Rosenberg, L. (2000). *Living in the light of death.* Boston, MA: Shambhala Publications.

Rosenberg, L. (1998). *Breath by breath.* Boston, MA: Shambhala Publications.

Rosenberg, M. (2003). *Nonviolent communication: A language of life.* Encinitas, CA: Puddle Dancer Press.

Rothberg, D. (2006). *The engaged spiritual life.* Boston, MA: Beacon Press.

Seligman, M. (2006). *Learned optimism.* New York, NY: Vintage.

Shapiro, .S.L. & Carlson, L.E. (2009). *The art and science of mindfulness: Integrating mindfulness into psychology and the helping professions (1st edition).* Washington, DC: American Psychological Association.

Stone, H. & Stone, S. (1993). *Embracing your inner critic.* New York, NY: Harper San Francisco.

Tart, C. (1994). *Living the mindful life.* Boston, MA: Shambhala Publications.

Tolle, E. (2008). *A new earth.* New York, NY: Penguin.

Tolle, E. (1999). *The power of now.* Novato, CA: New World Library.

Trungpa, C. (1993). *Training the mind.* Boston, MA: Shambhala Publications.

Williams, M., Teasdale, J., Segal, Z. & Kabat-Zinn, J. (2007). *The mindful way through depression.* New York, NY: The Guilford Press.

# Index

# About the Author

Phil Blustein MD, FRCP(C) has been a gastroenterologist —a medical specialist in gastrointestinal diseases—for more than thirty years. He has also intensively studied both Buddhism and modern psychology. Over the years, he has come to recognize how stress is one of the most important causes of medical symptoms and disease. Western medicine is wonderful at treating disease, but it doesn't get to the root cause of many health-related problems. In his practice, Dr. Blustein has seen that helping his patients identify and deal with their stress has really helped them to better manage their illnesses. He has written *Mindfulness Medication* to assist people in understanding and reducing their stress levels in order to provide some relief from their medical problems.

For further "Mindfulness Medication" prescriptions, including how-to videos, guided meditations and the latest tips, updates and interviews, follow Dr. Blustein and The Breath Project team's ongoing efforts to reduce stress at: <**www.thebreathproject.org**>.

If you would like to purchase additional print copies of this book, or downlad a pdf-based e-book version, please visit:
**<www.thebreathproject.org>**